Louisa Alcott

Girl of Old Boston

Illustrated by Claudine Nankivel

Louisa Alcott

Girl of Old Boston

By Jean Brown Wagoner

THE **BOBBS-MERRILL** COMPANY, INC.
A SUBSIDIARY OF HOWARD W. SAMS & CO., INC.
Publishers · INDIANAPOLIS · NEW YORK

To my sister
Louise B. Atherton

Like Louisa in the book, she
shares with others all the
good things of life

Illustrations

Numerous smaller illustrations

Contents

Books by Jean Brown Wagoner

ABIGAIL ADAMS: A GIRL OF COLONIAL DAYS
JANE ADDAMS: LITTLE LAME GIRL
JESSIE FREMONT: GIRL OF CAPITOL HILL
JULIA WARD HOWE: GIRL OF OLD NEW YORK
LOUISA ALCOTT: GIRL OF OLD BOSTON
MARTHA WASHINGTON: GIRL OF OLD VIRGINIA

Louisa Alcott

Girl of Old Boston

Louisa

IT WAS unusually quiet in the Alcott home. Father was in his study, writing. Mother was in the nursery with baby Elizabeth, and Anna and Louisa were in their playroom. Suddenly there was a terrific noise. Father rushed from the study. Anna and Louisa were screaming at the top of their lungs.

Father ran to the playroom. "What is the matter?" he cried.

The two little girls were fighting each other like a pair of wildcats.

"Children! Children! This is no way for sisters to act." Father tried to separate them.

"She won't give me the rocking chair!" shrieked Louisa.

"It's mine!"

"I was in it first!"

"You weren't either!"

"Was too."

"Wait, wait," broke in Father. "Anna, you're the older. Don't you think you should give up the chair to your younger sister?"

"I always have to give up," wailed Anna. "She pinched me, too."

"You come into the study with me. We'll leave Louisa in here by herself. Maybe if she thinks about it she'll be sorry and let you have the chair."

Anna dutifully went along with Father. She sat in front of the fire and waited. Louisa didn't call, though. She kept the chair all the rest of the afternoon.

"We must help Louisa control her temper,"

said Father that evening. "She's nearly three years old and grows naughtier every day."

"I have tried every way I know to correct her," Mother said, with a great sigh. "I have talked to her and scolded her, and even whipped her. The other day I shut her up in a dark closet. She thought that was great fun and begged me today to shut her up in the closet again. I don't know what to try next."

"I'll take her to school. Perhaps that will help discipline her."

Father took Louisa to his school before she was three years old.

All this happened in Boston many years ago, in 1835. The Alcotts were well known there. Father was a famous schoolmaster. Mother had grown up there. Louisa was well known, too, but for a different reason—she was always in trouble. From the time she could crawl she had been in mischief.

Once, before she was two, she was lost on board a ship on the family's trip down the Delaware River from Philadelphia to Boston. Her father and mother and everybody thought she had fallen overboard. They found her at last in the engine room, black and dirty from coal dust and covered with grease.

Louisa wanted something going on all the time. If things were too quiet, she pulled the covers off the tables. She had learned that all kinds of things happened then.

She was always asking questions. If her mother was busy and didn't answer her, she ran to the cradle where the baby was asleep and cried, "I'll wake the baby!"

Now that she was nearly three it was high time she learned to mend her ways.

Father took Louisa to the school which he taught. They didn't have far to go.

Most schools were ugly. The children sat on

hard wooden benches. The walls and windows were black with smoke from the stove. There were no pictures, no storybooks, and no geographies with colored maps. The teacher was usually a cross old man with a whip in his hand. When the children didn't learn their lessons, he used the whip.

Louisa's father was not like that. He was always pleasant and never used a whip. He loved children and loved to teach them.

Louisa liked the schoolroom. It was warm and pretty. The windows were like those in a church. The walls were painted. The floor was covered with beautiful rugs. There were fine pictures and books all around the room.

There was no other school like this. People heard about it. They came from far and near to visit it. They couldn't believe their eyes. "The boys and girls of Mr. Alcott's school love to study," they said. "Whoever heard of such a thing? They learn faster than any other children in the country."

Many rich people sent their children to Mr. Alcott. They paid him a great deal of money. He bought more books and fine statues.

Mr. Alcott not only taught the children to read and write and spell—he taught them more than that. He taught them to be kind to one another and to love beautiful things. They were happy boys and girls.

The people of Boston were proud of Mr. Alcott and his school. Louisa's mother was wise to send her there.

THE FIRST LESSON

After school, between teatime and supper, Father worked in his study. He was writing a book about Anna and Elizabeth and Louisa. Each day he wrote down what they were doing.

17

Louisa liked to sit on the floor beside her father and pretend to write, too. She "wrote" busily in all the books within her reach. Other times she played with the big, heavy books as though they were blocks, and built towers and walls and bridges with them. If a book happened to open at a picture, she took it to her father and laid it on his knee.

"Read this to Weezie," she would say.

"After supper, Louisa, not now," he would reply.

One evening Louisa marched over to her father. She pushed his pen away and with her hands covered the page on which he was writing. "Read now, not after," she demanded crossly.

Father looked serious. He held one of her hands down on the paper. Then he took a pencil and carefully drew a line around the little fist. When she took her hand away, there was the out-

18

line of it on the page. Father wrote beneath it, "Louisa's hand."

"It doesn't look like a bad little hand, does it?" he said.

"It isn't bad. It's a good hand and 'longs to Weezie," said Louisa sturdily.

"I saw it push Father's hand away just now, so he couldn't work. That was bad," said Mr. Alcott. "Today I saw it pinch somebody, like this." He pinched Louisa's cheek hard.

She didn't cry, but her lips trembled and her eyes were big with tears.

"That hurt, didn't it?" he asked.

Louisa nodded.

"Was it nice of me to do that to you?"

"No, that wasn't fair," said Louisa.

"Do you know why I did it?"

" 'Cause Weezie did it to Anna."

"Had Anna hurt you?"

Louisa hung her head. "No," she whispered.

19

"Then that wasn't fair either, was it?"

The little girl stood ashamed and silent.

"What shall we do to make this hand kind and gentle?"

"Cut it off?" suggested Louisa, hiding her hand behind her.

"No, no," replied Father. "It couldn't do *anything* then, could it?"

Louisa thought a moment, then spoke brightly. "Weezie can play she's Mother, then her hands will be soft."

"Why, that is the very thing," agreed Father happily. "No one's hands are busier or kinder than Mother's. Why is that?"

"'Cause Mother's more kinder than anybody," came the answer.

"Always remember that, daughter. When you're angry and want to pinch someone or throw something, just say to yourself, 'Mother wouldn't do that.' It will help you guide your hands."

20

Later, as soon as supper was over, Louisa opened her storybook to her favorite picture and ran with it to Father. "Now read," she said, and pushed the book into his hands.

Anna had brought a book too. She gave it to him at the same time.

Louisa pushed her and said, "Mine first."

"I was here first," said Anna.

Louisa jumped at Anna. "I'll pinch you," she scolded—then stopped herself. She turned and smiled at Father. "Weezie forgot." Then she picked up Anna's book and gave it to him.

He was so pleased that he took her by the hands and danced a jig with her. Anna and Mother looked on in astonishment, then they joined in too. Lizzie clapped her hands.

"This is fun," thought Louisa. "I'm going to be good all the time."

"Louisa has learned her first lesson," thought Father.

Louisa's Birthday Party

Louisa lay in bed thinking, "I'm going to be as good as I can be today. This is my birthday. I am four years old now and I'm going to have a party for my birthday."

She jumped out of bed. The floor was icy cold. She looked out of the window and saw great flurries of snow. She decided to hop back into bed again for a while.

Louisa heard Father making a fire in the fireplace downstairs. There were fireplaces in every room. At night Father would cover the fires with ashes. In the morning he poked them and uncovered the red-hot embers. He piled on fresh wood. Soon the fires would be blazing and the rooms would be warm.

Today Louisa was too excited to lie still and wait for a fire. She jumped up again and ran to the washstand in the corner of the room.

Louisa tipped the pitcher to pour water into the basin. No water ran out. She looked inside. A film of ice covered the top of the water.

"Oh, goody!" she cried. "I love cold water!" She broke the ice, poured the water, and washed and splashed to her heart's content.

By that time she felt so lively she had to have someone to play with. She looked over at Anna. Anna was still in bed. Louisa took a piece of ice and let it melt down Anna's neck.

"Ow!" squealed Anna, and hid her head under the pillow. Then began a tug of war. Louisa pulled one end of the pillow. Anna pulled the other. Suddenly Anna let go. Louisa went tumbling head over heels.

Mother called upstairs. "No time for play this morning. Have you forgotten what day this is, Louisa?"

Louisa hurried into her clothes and ran downstairs. She hugged her mother and danced around her father. She ran to the kitchen to see what Cook had for breakfast. Louisa loved breakfast in the winter. The warm applesauce, muffins, and the cereal smelled good. It seemed to her that the rest of the family never would be ready to sit down to eat. She ran outdoors and played in the snow till Cook called her.

As soon as breakfast was over, Anna and Louisa ran back upstairs and made their beds. This was not easy to do. The sheets were as cold as ice and made their fingers numb. They made their room neat, then went back downstairs to run errands for Mother. After that, Anna got out her books to study a little before she went to school. Louisa didn't get out her books. She didn't have to go to school today because it was her birthday.

Soon Father and Anna bundled up in their warm wraps and left for school. Mother was busy in the kitchen. Louisa went into the library to play with her father's books.

Mother brought in the cradle and let Lizzie watch Louisa at her play. Louisa peeked at her now and then. Baby tried to reach her through the sides of the cradle.

Louisa decided to let her play with the books, too. She lifted the baby out of the cradle and laid her down in the midst of the books. She built towers and let Lizzie kick them over.

Then Louisa built a wall around her. At first it was a low wall, but Louisa made it higher. Finally it was so high that she couldn't see over it. She looked at Baby through a crack. Lizzie lay quite still looking all about. Then she spied Louisa. She clapped her hands and laughed.

Louisa played peekaboo with her for a long time. After a while she pulled a heavy piece of wrapping paper over the top of the wall. That made it so dark inside she couldn't see Lizzie. She waited to see what would happen. She thought, "Maybe Baby won't like this new game. Maybe she thinks she is in a dark prison or something."

While she was waiting, Mother called, "Louisa, would you like to watch me make the cakes for your birthday party?"

Away Louisa flew. She forgot all about Lizzie and the paper and the books.

In the kitchen Mother was ready to begin. She had scooped the sugar from the barrel. It was hard and lumpy and yellow. She put the sugar in a heavy cloth bag. Then she used the hammer and pounded it to break up the lumps. She poured the sugar onto the breadboard and rolled it with the rolling pin until it was soft and fine. She creamed the sugar and butter together, then stirred in the eggs and flour and milk until she had a smooth batter.

The excited Louisa leaned her elbows on the kitchen table and watched. Every now and then she stuck her finger into the bowl and took a taste. My, but it was good!

When the little cakes were all baked and iced, Mother let Louisa sprinkle them with red sugar. They were the prettiest birthday cakes Louisa had ever seen.

"Now, I must feed little Lizzie," said Mother. "She has finished her nap by this time." Mother ran in to lift the baby from the cradle. When she got there, she cried out, "Why, where is she? Where is my baby?"

She threw the covers back. She looked under the cradle. She looked about the room. There was no baby in sight. Louisa heard her and came running from the kitchen.

"Oh, Louisa, I can't find Lizzie!"

Louisa's mind was full of pretty, red-sugared cakes. She hardly heard her mother. She followed her about while Mother rushed from room to room. Cook joined the search. No Lizzie was to be found. Mother was out of breath and frightened.

All at once Louisa remembered. "Oh, I know where Lizzie is! She's in a big black dungeon."

The cook shrieked.

Mother took Louisa by the hand. "Quick, Louisa. Show me where she is."

Louisa led them to the library and pointed to the tower of books. "There!" she said.

Mother rushed over and pulled the paper away. She was about to scold Louisa soundly for this prank, but inside the tower of books little Elizabeth lay fast asleep. She opened her eyes. When she saw Louisa peeking at her, she thought they were still playing. She laughed so merrily

28

that Mother didn't have the heart to scold Louisa. Baby's sleep on the floor inside the wall hadn't hurt her.

Mother explained to Louisa later that it wasn't a safe place to leave their precious baby. Louisa didn't do it again.

Mother was nearly as glad as Louisa when it was time for her to dress for the party.

"You will have to stand still, Louisa, or I can't button your dress," said Mother. "Don't you want the party to begin? The children are waiting for you at the school."

Then Louisa hugged herself tight and stood still. Mother tied a pink ribbon in her hair and put a pink sash around her waist. Then they went to the school.

When the children saw Louisa, they danced around her and sang, "Happy Birthday! Happy Birthday!" Anna ran to her and hugged her.

Then Father called out, "Follow the leader,"

and the fun began. He played the leader and everybody fell in line behind him. He led them in all kinds of funny exercises. He jumped over his desk. He turned handsprings. He climbed in and out of the windows. The older boys had to help Louisa over the desk and lift her in and out of the windows, but she turned handsprings better than anybody. They played Drop the Handkerchief and Spin the Plate. All at once it was time for refreshments.

Louisa's father called her to him. He lifted her onto a table. The children lined up in front of her. One of the girls put a crown on her head. They all sang a song they had learned just for her. Then Mother brought in the cakes. How the children clapped their hands when they saw them!

Louisa passed one to each guest. She could hardly wait to come to the end of the line. How fast the cakes disappeared!

Louisa looked at her mother. "There aren't enough to go around," she whispered.

"Oh, surely there are," replied Mother. She counted too.

Louisa was right. There was only one cake left. She came to the last guest, a little boy. She covered the cake with her hand and wouldn't pass it to him. He stood waiting.

"It is my party," she said to herself. "I ought to have a cake more than anybody."

Mother put her arms around Louisa. "It is always best to give away the nice things," she said. "I'm sure Louisa won't let her little friend go without."

Then Louisa gave the boy the last little cake. Mother gave Louisa a kiss.

Letters Tell Stories

"I DON'T LIKE letters. I wish they had never been born," Louisa said with a sigh one night. She was studying her reading lesson for the next day. All the Alcotts were in the living room as usual. Supper was over and the fun of the day was about to begin. Tonight, Father had a new story to read to them, and Anna and Louisa were going to act out a little play about King Midas and the Golden Touch.

They were all waiting for Louisa to finish.

"You surely don't mean that you don't like letters," said Father. "You like stories, and letters tell stories."

"They don't tell me anything." Louisa made a face at the letter S. She had a great deal of trouble remembering it.

Father wrote the letter on her slate. "What does it look like?" he asked.

"A wiggle-worm," replied Louisa.

"What is another thing that crawls along the ground?" Father got down and wriggled along the floor. He hissed and moved his head from side to side.

"I know, I know!" shouted Louisa. "S stands for snake. It makes a s-s-s-s sound and it wriggles. I won't forget S again.

"Here is another letter I can't remember. Please act it out."

It was the letter *I*. Father stood in the middle of the room. He held himself stiff as a poker and puffed out his cheeks and stuck out his chest in a most important way. Then he strutted proudly across the room.

34

"*I* am Mr. Know-it-all," he began. "*I* want attention. *I* have my way. *I* rule the——"

"I know! I know now!" sang Louisa. "The stiff letter that doesn't bend any place is *I*."

"Do some more, please, Father," begged Anna. "You look so funny."

Father was busy for a while and Louisa learned a lot of new letters that night. She made him do Y over and over. He stood on his head and spread his legs apart for Y. The letter X was done by standing with his arms and legs spread wide apart.

Z was the funniest letter of all. Father zigzagged across the room. He pretended to zoom about like a bee, buzzing in Baby's ear, *b-z-z-z-*ing around Mother's geranium plants in the window. He bent himself at the knees and the hips till he was shaped like a Z. By that time, he was worn out.

"I like letters now," said Louisa. "I can

35

hardly wait for tomorrow's lesson. If I forget at school, will you act out some of them again?" she asked hopefully.

"You won't forget them from now on." He smiled. Father was not sure that this plan would work so well in a schoolroom. It was just a little too much fun for everybody but the teacher.

THE FROG POND

Louisa sat in the schoolroom and wished that she were outdoors. She could see the new green leaves on the trees on the Common, and hear the frogs croaking at the pond. It was hard to sit still and keep quiet but Father didn't allow any noise whatsoever when the other children were studying.

Father must have guessed what Louisa wanted, for he wrote her a note and laid it on her slate. It said: "Does Louisa want to play? Then

36

tiptoe softly to the door. Play hard for a while. Then come back."

"What a nice man my father is," Louisa said to herself. No one noticed when she stole out of the door. Away she flew to the Common.

The Common was a wonderful place to play. There were walks and paths all through it. Louisa liked to romp upon the grass and make friends with people passing by. Sometimes she just sat looking up at the tall stately elms.

Along near-by Beacon Street passed a steady parade of light produce carts, loaded farm wagons, and shiny carriages. In the carriages rode ladies dressed in beautiful gowns with spreading skirts and carrying tiny parasols to protect their faces from the sun's rays.

Louisa liked the scissors grinder, jingling a bell as he walked slowly along, and the fruit sellers crying their wares. Often the town crier came by, ringing his bell and calling out his latest news.

37

As much as Louisa loved to watch the interesting sights, though, she could not sit still for a very long time. Soon she was roaming around again.

Near the middle of the Common there was a pond. It was shaded by tall trees which were reflected in the calm water. Louisa loved to throw pebbles into the pond, then watch the ripples spread across the surface.

Children knew better than to wade or try to swim in the pond, because it was swampy and full of weeds. There was no bottom to it. It was just deep oozing mud. It was called the Frog Pond.

Louisa knew how dangerous this place was, but she liked to play near it and listen to the frogs. This morning she skipped along the edge of it. She was thinking, "How fine it is to be running about in the park."

Suddenly she slipped. She had not noticed

how near the edge she was. Her feet flew out from under her. Before she could cry out or grab hold of anything, she was in the water.

She felt the weeds pull her down. The mud sucked at her feet. The black water closed over her head. In only a few seconds she realized her father couldn't come to her. Mother was home with the baby. No one would ever know what had become of her. She was drowning. She struggled for breath.

Just then two strong arms reached under her. The next thing she knew she was on the bank. She looked up into the smiling face of a young Negro boy. He had seen Louisa fall in. Without thinking of the danger to his own life he had jumped in after her. Other people had seen, too. They ran to the pond in time to see the boy pull her out. They carried Louisa home.

Mother hugged her joyously and kissed her muddy little face.

Father had seen people running. He hurried home from school.

"What has happened?" he cried.

"Louisa fell into the Frog Pond," everybody explained. "She would have drowned, without a doubt, but a Negro boy saved her. He pulled her out. It is a miracle that he found her."

"Where is he?" asked Father.

No one knew.

"What's his name? Who was he?" he asked.

No one knew. Mr. Alcott asked everywhere. He wanted to thank the boy who had saved his daughter's life. He never found him, but he never forgot him. Louisa never forgot, either.

THE RUNAWAY

When Louisa was nearly six, she noticed that things were different at home.

Mother began to do all the housework. The

cook left. The maid left. Mother cooked and ironed and cleaned and sewed.

Louisa began to ask questions. She followed Mother about. "Mother, why do you work so hard?" she asked. "Why don't you put on your pretty dress and walk with us in the park any more? Why don't we have tea parties in front of the fire, the way we used to do?"

"I don't believe you can understand, Louisa, but I shall try to explain it to you. People are having hard times. They can't pay your father for teaching their children any more. They simply haven't any money."

"Why don't they work and get the money? They're bad people not to pay. Father works very hard to teach their children."

"Hush, Louisa. They can't find work. There isn't any work. It isn't anyone's fault."

Louisa was not satisfied. She kept on asking questions. Mother was tired. Louisa's questions

41

bothered her. "Go get your hoop and run and play," she said.

This was what Louisa wanted. She loved to roll an iron hoop from a barrel, pushing it along with a stick. She ran beside the hoop to guide it and keep it going as long as she could. It was great fun and hard to do. The streets were full of boys with hoops, but not a boy could keep up with Louisa.

Other mothers didn't let their little girls play on the Common. Girls were supposed to play in the house with dolls, or they learned to embroider and sew. Louisa didn't want to be bothered with dolls or with sewing. She wanted to be outdoors running and jumping and rolling hoops and playing ball.

The harder Mother worked the oftener Louisa skipped out to play. Rain or shine, hot or cold, Louisa was ready for a romp in the park. She made friends with everybody. All the children

42

knew her. It made no difference to her whether they were rich or poor, dirty or clean, little or big, just so they let her play with them.

Often Louisa had such a good time that she forgot to come home for lunch. Mother worried when she stayed out too long. She didn't have time to look for the child. Father had to go after her when he came home. Sometimes he found her far from home.

Mother scolded Louisa. "It is naughty of you to run away," she said.

"I don't mean to run away," said Louisa. "I just forget."

Times grew harder. The Alcotts had to move into a smaller house in a different neighborhood.

One day Louisa followed her new friends to the city dump, a place to which people carried their ashes and trash. It was the first time she had seen this place. She thought it was wonderful. She found all kinds of funny things to look at.

Lunchtime came before she knew it. The other children said, "Eat with us. We have plenty." They built a fire out on the dump, and baked potatoes in the ashes. They had hard, stale bread. They shared with Louisa. She thought she had never tasted such good food.

Finally Louisa began to get tired. She wanted to go home and tell her mother about the new playground she had found. She wanted Mother to know her new friends.

Louisa couldn't find the way home.

She was not frightened. "Father will soon find me," she said to herself. "He always does."

The other children had left. It began to grow cold. Louisa started to walk along the street.

"If I walk far enough, I shall come to my home," she thought. She walked until she was too tired to go farther. It was growing dark. She saw a lamplighter far down the street. She ran to meet him as he moved along with his short

ladder on his back. At every po
up his ladder, climb up and light

Louisa always loved to watch for
lighter from a window of her house and
him as he went by.

"He will show me the way home," she said
herself now. But this was not the lamplighter
that she knew. He had no idea where she lived,
and went on down the street. Louisa was alone
again. She was tired and cold and hungry.

A big, shaggy-haired dog came and stood beside her. He licked her face. She put her arms
around his neck. He felt nice and warm. He lay
down beside her. Louisa rested her head on the
dog. He made a nice pillow. "I'll wait here for
Father," she decided. Soon she fell fast asleep.

She woke up suddenly. It was dark. She
couldn't remember where she was. A bell was
ringing near by. A man was calling something
over and over in a loud voice. "Lost, lost! A

45

'n a pink frock, white hat,

ied and ran to the man.
as the town crier. He

ked for her all after-
grow dark, they were
, so they went to the town crier.
was a man with a good strong voice. He carried a bell with him. He walked through the
streets ringing the bell and crying out the news.
When people heard the bell, they ran to their
doors and windows to hear what he had to say.

Father told the crier how Louisa was dressed,
how old she was, and where she lived. The crier
started out at once with his bell.

When he found Louisa, he did not take her
home at once. He said, "It is a long way to your
house. You will be too tired to walk there until
you've had something to eat. My home is near.

46

I'll take you to my wife. She'll give you some supper. Then I'll take you home."

The town crier's wife was kind to Louisa. She gave her molasses and bread on a pretty tin plate. The plate had the letters of the alphabet around the edge. The crier's wife was surprised that Louisa could read them so easily.

"Oh, I could read long ago," said Louisa. "My father taught me when I was little."

The woman thought that Louisa was still a pretty little girl.

When Louisa started home, she wanted to take the dog with her. "He likes me," she said. "See how he looks at me and how he wags his tail. I'll take him with me."

"No, no. He belongs to a boy who lives near," said the crier.

"I want him anyway," said Louisa. "He'll feel sad if I leave him behind. Ask the little boy if I can have him. See, he won't stay behind."

"We must get started," said the crier. "Your poor mother will be sick with worry."

Louisa began to cry. "I want to take the dog along," she insisted.

"What's this?" spoke up the wife. "What a sight! A big girl who can read and write crying like a baby!"

That hushed Louisa right away. She stopped crying and patted the dog good-by. Then she thanked the woman for her supper and trotted off with the crier.

What a thankful mother took a tired little Louisa into her arms that night! How Father shook the crier's hand! Anna came running downstairs in her nightcap and gown. Lizzie woke up and pattered down the steps, calling, "Come, tell me."

After they were all safe in bed, Louisa told Anna and Lizzie about the dump, the baked potatoes, the tin plate, and the friendly dog.

49

"Tomorrow," said Lizzie, after Louisa had told them everything, "I'll go to the dump, too, with Weezie. We'll both get lost."

"No, no," said Anna. "Poor mother has been too worried. She cried and cried when she couldn't find you, Louisa."

That made Louisa cry too.

She felt important the next morning. Everyone made such a fuss over her. That didn't last long, though. Mother decided that she needed to learn a lesson. It was high time that she remembered to stay nearer home.

"There'll be no more runaways," Mother said.

She took Louisa to the front room where everybody who looked in the door would see her. She tied one end of a piece of string to Louisa's wrist. She tied the other end to the arm of the sofa. All day she left her there. She even brought her lunch to her.

Everybody stared at Louisa. Mother said,

"Louisa runs away just as our kitten does, so we have to tie her up."

Louisa had plenty of time to think that over. She decided she wanted to be treated like Mother's little girl and not like a pet animal.

Late in the afternoon, when no one was near, she called out, "I'm sorry I worried you, Mother. I surely will never forget again. Do you think you can love me a little?"

Then Mother took Louisa in her arms and kissed her and hugged her tight. "Of course, I love my dear little runaway," she said. "I'm sure we'll never have to do this again."

They didn't, either.

A Shared
Breakfast

PEOPLE EVERYWHERE were poor the winter that
Louisa was seven. There was very little money
and almost no work. Mr. Alcott was paid less
and less for teaching and life at the Alcotts' was
very bare indeed.

Not having a stove, they had to cook at the
fireplace. They had less food on the table.
There was enough, though, of good wholesome
food, and they had such merry times that at
first they didn't really notice how plain the meals
had become.

After a while Anna and Louisa grew tired of
having the same thing over and over. They

missed the tasty puddings and pies. That wasn't the worst of it—there came a time when there wasn't any sugar in the house.

One morning Louisa threw down her spoon and complained crossly, "I'm tired of rice without any sugar. I want a cinnamon roll and muffins with butter and jelly."

"We used to have good things all the time," said Anna. "Now we don't have anything but rice and more rice and more rice, and sometimes just dry bread."

"Rice is a good wholesome food, my dears," said Mother cheerfully. "It is much better for you without sugar."

The two little girls didn't answer. They just sat there and wouldn't eat.

Then Father said, "There are little children near us who will be glad to have your breakfast. These are dreadful times. People are starving all around here." He rose from the table, his bowl

53

of rice in his hands. "Put on your wraps, girls," he said. "Then bring your bowls of rice with you and come along with me."

Father went out of the house. Anna followed him, carrying her bowl, and Louisa followed Anna. People turned to stare at the strange parade. Father led the girls down the street to a neat little frame house. He knocked gently on the door.

A thin, stooped woman answered at once. When she saw who was there, and when she spied the steaming bowls, she cried out, "God bless you, Mr. Alcott!" Then she called, "Come boys, come! Here are Mr. Alcott and his daughters with food for you."

Two pale little boys ran to the door. Their eyes opened wide when they saw what Anna and Louisa carried. The girls handed them each a bowl and watched them gulp down the food. The boys were so grateful that Anna and Louisa were sorry they hadn't brought last night's supper, too.

"We shall come again soon," they promised. "We shall bring you our share of the pudding on Sunday. Mother makes the best bread pudding in the whole world."

On the way back home Louisa asked curiously, "Is their father out of work? Is that why they were so hungry?"

"No, it is worse than that," Father replied in a serious voice. "Their father has work, but he drinks. When he is drunk, he forgets about his little boys. Often there is no wood in the house, either, to keep them warm."

"Then, Father," said Louisa stoutly, "each day you must tell us whether they have food or not. Every day I shall give one of my meals to those poor children."

"So shall I," said Anna. "We'll share one meal each day with somebody who is hungry."

"That's the way I like to hear my little girls talk," said Father. "Mother will be very, very proud of you."

Many and many a day after that people saw the Alcotts carrying food to the hungry.

SOME CHANGES

"We shall have school here at home today," said Father one morning.

"Why, what will the children at the school do?" asked Anna.

"There isn't any school," said Father sadly.

"Is the beautiful school gone?"

He nodded.

Louisa began to cry. "Where are your books, and the pictures, and your fine desk?"

"They are gone just while times are bad," Father assured her. "It costs a great deal of money to have a school like that. In the meantime, I'll teach you each morning before I have to go to work. This morning Mother and I have a surprise for you." He brought out two little books and gave one to each of them.

"Why, there isn't any writing in mine," said Louisa.

"Nor in mine," Anna chimed in.

"You are to do the writing yourselves," he said. "You must write in your books each day."

"What shall I write?" asked Louisa.

"Write about the things you want to remember. Write your thoughts. Write about anything that troubles you. It will help you clear your mind to write down what you worry about. Put in the book the everyday happenings here at home. These are to be your diaries. I want you to keep them all your lives."

That is how Louisa started her first book.

The school did not open again. Anna and Louisa learned their lessons at home. They didn't go to any other school. Besides the lessons they learned in books, they learned to sweep and dust and cook and sew.

Anna loved to help keep house. She was quick to learn. Louisa didn't like housework.

"I should have been a boy," she said. "I wasn't meant to be a girl. I like to climb trees and jump fences and run like the wind."

More and more often she slipped out of the house and left her share of the work to Anna. Anna didn't mind. When Louisa came home, she always had exciting adventures to tell. She whispered them each night to Anna after they went to bed.

ADVENTURE ON THE DOCK

One day Louisa didn't come home.

"I am afraid something has happened to her," Mother said to Father when he returned from work. "I do not believe she has run away. I have called and called but she does not answer."

Father immediately started on the run toward the water front.

The Alcotts had moved again. This time they lived closed to the ocean. They could look out and see the boats and the shipping at the docks. Louisa loved to play on the docks where she could see all that was going on.

There was a piano factory close by. At the side of the factory was a long, sloping runway. It was used to wheel pianos down to the dock where they were loaded into ships or into moving vans. At the top of the runway were large wooden packing cases in which the pianos were shipped.

Louisa liked to run up and down the runway. This particular day she saw some boys get into one of the packing cases and go rolling down the runway in it. The big box rolled faster and faster down the slope and ended in a great crash at the bottom of the runway.

"Oh, they must all be killed," thought Louisa in a fright.

The boys weren't hurt at all. "It's fun," they shouted. "It makes a terrible noise when it hits the bottom, but you just hold on tight. It shakes you up a little, that's all. Of course, no girl would dare to do it," they added. They said that purposely to tease Louisa.

Louisa immediately ran up and tried to start one of the cases down by herself.

"Wait, wait!" cried Will, one of the older boys. "Don't try it. We were only teasing. We didn't mean for you to try to do it."

"You did it. I know I can do it, too," said Louisa stubbornly.

"Someone must go with you to push it and get it started straight. If you are not careful, you will roll off the edge and be killed."

"Then come here and start it for me," said Louisa impatiently.

"I don't think your mother would like it," Will said honestly.

"Hurry up," insisted Louisa. "Don't be a sissy." She stepped into the packing case.

Will gave it a push and jumped in, too.

What a roar and rumble there were inside the case! What a tremendous crash it made at the bottom! Louisa loved it.

"Let's do it again," she begged. So they did it again, then again and again, until it became only tame sport.

"Let's try rolling down in a barrel," said Louisa. "That would be much faster."

"Yes, and it would also be much more dangerous," said Will. "You couldn't jump out and stop yourself if you went too close to the edge. I won't let you do it, Louisa!"

"Let her try it," said another boy, who had a mean, sly look. He rolled a barrel to the top of the runway for Louisa. She got into it.

"Please don't do it," begged Will.

The second boy said, "You keep out of this, Will! Just because you're a 'fraid-cat doesn't need to make her one, too."

That decided Louisa. She was flattered by his

words. "Give me a push," she called from inside the barrel.

The mean boy gave the barrel a nudge with his foot. He didn't take care to start it straight at all. The barrel rolled toward the edge of the runway. Will shouted. He sprang after it, tried to stop it, but barely touched it. Faster and faster it rolled toward the edge. It seemed fairly to fly through the air, and then it *was* flying through the air. Halfway down it bounded off the runway, crashed to the ground below, and broke into many pieces.

The boys couldn't bear to look to see what had happened to Louisa. There was no sound from under the wreck. Some of them crawled down to look under the splintered wood.

Sobbing, Will said, "She was such a jolly little girl. I shouldn't have let her do it. I'm older. I knew better."

The mean boy said, "Oh, she ain't hurt."

"If she is, I'll give you the thrashing of your life," said Will.

The mean boy ran away.

By this time the rest of the boys had reached the barrel. They lifted off the broken pieces. Louisa lay under them, still and white.

All the boys ran away then, except Will. He called after them to go for her father. They were so badly frightened, they ran away and hid. "We might be put in jail," they said, "because we let her go down in the barrel and get hurt."

Will was afraid to lift Louisa. He feared he would hurt her. He didn't want to leave her, either. He just sat there and called for help.

Father heard him and came running. The boy told him all that had happened.

Father leaned over Louisa. "She's alive," he said, "but I can't tell how badly she's hurt."

Will helped Father drag a wide board to where Louisa lay. Father lifted her onto it. He

64

sent Will for help and men came quickly. One ran for a doctor, another to warn Mrs. Alcott, and others helped carry Louisa home. When they had carried her inside the house and laid her down, she opened her eyes and was astonished to see everybody gathered about her. She looked at the doctor.

"Who's hurt? What's the matter?" she asked, and sat up. Then everyone else was astonished.

The doctor looked Louisa over carefully. She was hardly hurt at all. The wind had been knocked out of her and there was a bump on her head. The next day she was as good as new!

Louisa's Reward

ONE EVENING after Anna and Louisa had gone to bed, Mother and Father had a talk.

"Louisa is growing into a regular tomboy," said Mother worriedly. "She plays in the streets day in and day out."

"She doesn't run away any more," said Father.

"No, but she wants to be outdoors all the time. She loses her temper more and more easily. The children in this neighborhood play too roughly. The boys tease her and put her up to all kinds of pranks. I wish she would play quietly at home with Anna and her little friends. They have such good times with their dolls.

"That's too tame for our Louisa," said Father, "but it isn't right for the boys to tease her. Perhaps we'd better give her a vacation."

"I'll let her visit our friends the Carletons in Providence. They have often begged me to send them one of my girls for a while. The change will do Louisa good."

"We'll let her go as a reward for not running away," said Father.

A few days after this talk, Mother asked Louisa, "How would you like to go on a trip?"

"You mean go clear away in a stagecoach?" asked Louisa. "How soon do I start?" She ran about the house, upstairs and down, gathering her belongings together. She thought she was leaving in a few minutes.

"Oh, you have plenty of time," said Mother. "You can't leave until Saturday. Anna, do you think you and I can manage the house by ourselves?"

Anna wanted to go on the trip, too, but she was proud that Mother counted on her help. "I'll take all the care of Lizzie while Louisa is gone," she said sweetly.

Lizzie had been listening. Now she ran and hugged Anna about the knees so tight that Anna fell down. Louisa tripped over Anna. Lizzie saw them both on the floor, so she fell down on top of Louisa.

Father came in at that moment. He saw the children on the floor, so he said, "What kind of game is this?" Then he pretended to stumble and fall down, too.

Mother laughed to see her family in such high spirits. Then everybody jumped up and helped Mother get the supper on the table. They were all so happy making plans for Louisa's vacation that nobody noticed how skimpy the evening meal was. The boiled rice smelled and tasted unusually good. They scraped the kettle clean.

Louisa was awake long before daylight Saturday morning. She listened for Mother, but didn't hear her moving about. "I wonder if Mother has overslept," she thought. "Perhaps she has forgotten that this is the day I leave."

Louisa got up and dressed. Mother had packed most of her things the night before. Louisa put her nightgown and hairbrush and bedroom slippers in her trunk and closed it. It was a little too heavy for her to carry, so she dragged it down the stairs *thump, thump, thump.* She pulled it across the living room and set it outside the front door. Then she put on her coat and hat and sat down on the doorstep to wait until time for the coach.

"*I'm* not going to be late," Louisa resolved to herself.

Mother came downstairs a little later. "I'll make muffins this morning," she thought.

"Louisa is fond of them and I'll have them as a going-away surprise."

Father and Lizzie came to the table when Mother called out that breakfast was ready. "Where's Louisa?" she asked.

"She was already dressed and gone when I got up," said Anna.

"Why, I haven't seen her," said Mother anxiously. "Surely Louisa hasn't run away this morning, of all mornings."

Father called loudly. There was no answer. "I'll take a look up and down the street. Louisa may have gone to tell some of her friends goodby," he said.

He opened the front door. There was Louisa, leaning against her trunk, sound asleep. He touched her shoulder gently to awaken her. She was astounded when she opened her eyes. She had been dreaming. She thought she had gone to Providence and come back already.

Blinking her eyes, she followed Father in to the breakfast table and sat down. Then, when she smelled the muffins, she sat up, wide-awake. She was as hungry as if she really had been on a journey.

Mother filled a lunch basket for her. She knew Louisa would be starving before she reached the end of her trip.

Louisa might have gone to Providence by train, but it cost more than by stagecoach. She had always wanted to ride in a coach. Now at last she was going to have her wish. The coaches were pulled by four fine big horses. The driver sat on a high seat in front. With one hand he handled the reins guiding the horses. In the other he wielded a great long whip which he cracked in the air above the horses' heads.

Mother, Father, Anna, and Elizabeth all went with Louisa to the street crossing where the coach passed. When they saw it coming, they all began to wave—Father waved his hat, Mother and the girls, their handkerchiefs.

For a moment Louisa thought the big horses were going to thunder by, but the driver pulled on the reins and shouted, "Whoa!" in a tremendous voice. The coach stopped beside them.

72

Father spoke to the driver. He told him where Louisa was going to stay in Providence.

The driver said, "I know the Carletons. I'll see that your little girl gets there safely."

Father was glad. He paid the driver and lifted Louisa into the coach. Then the driver cracked his whip and away they went.

Mother and Anna and Lizzie waved as long as the coach was in sight. Anna and Lizzie cried on the way back. "It's no fun at home without Louisa," they said.

Louisa didn't cry. She looked all around the inside of the coach. It wasn't so fine as she had expected. She had thought the seats would be covered with red velvet the way they were in the storybooks. They weren't. They were covered with black leather. The leather was old and torn and the stuffing showed in places.

She couldn't see anything but the sky out of the window, because the seat was so low. It was exciting, though, to feel the coach sway from side to side.

"We must be going very fast."

Louisa counted the people in the coach. She talked to each one, and asked where they were going and how long they were going to stay.

"How long will it take to get to Providence?" she asked a man across from her. "Are we nearly there?"

He laughed. "We've just started," he said.

"When can I get a drink?"

"The driver will stop to rest the horses at Woonsocket. You can get a drink there."

"How soon will we get to Woonsocket?"

"Pretty soon," the man replied patiently.

An elderly woman sat next to Louisa. She held a basket on her knees.

"What's in your basket?" asked Louisa.

The woman said, "Little girls should be seen and not heard."

"What does she mean by that?" Louisa asked her friend across the aisle.

"She thinks the little girl sitting next to her is talking too much," the man said, smiling.

Louisa didn't like that. She frowned and stuck out her lower lip. She said to herself, "I don't like that old lady. I hope she drops her basket. I hope it breaks open and spills everything in it all over every place."

Louisa didn't say anything more for a long time. She sulked and looked down her nose. Her little face that had been so bright and sunny looked like a thundercloud.

The coach rumbled along. Sometimes the road was rough and the coach would jolt and bump. Sometimes it was dark inside. Louisa could see branches of trees and thick foliage out the window. She knew they were going through forests. Pretty soon they went up a hill—Louisa could tell by the way the coach tipped endways.

The tops of the trees went down below the window sill. Then the trees came up again and the coach tipped up the other end. They were going down the other side of the hill. Louisa could not stay on the seat. She kept sliding off.

The elderly lady next to her did not notice. She was asleep. Louisa picked herself up off the floor a third time.

The basket on the woman's knees slipped and fell then. Louisa lifted it. It was not very heavy. It wobbled in a funny way. "There must be something alive in it," she guessed. She put it back on the seat.

Then the coach gave a great lurch. The basket fell with a thump. The catch on the lid broke and out tumbled a beautiful big cat.

Louisa let out a squeal of delight. She stooped to pick up the cat—she loved cats. The cat gave a great leap and sprang out the window, right over Louisa's head. Louisa screamed.

The woman awoke. "Oh, oh, oh!" she cried. "My beautiful, lovely cat. Where is it?"

"It jumped out the window," cried Louisa.

"It will be killed!" cried the lady. "Stop the coach!"

Louisa banged on the window under the driver's seat. "Stop! Stop!" she called.

The driver heard the screams. He shouted "Whoa! Whoa!" to the horses and pulled on the reins so hard that the horses stood on their hind legs. "The door must have come unlatched," he thought. "The little girl must have fallen out." He jumped down from his seat, ran to the side of the coach, and looked in.

"What's the matter?" he cried.

"This lady's cat!" cried Louisa. "It jumped out of the window. Open the door! I'll go back and get it for her."

"I'll do nothing of the kind," shouted the driver. "Hold up the coach for a cat? I guess not!" He was angry. "I've never been late getting into Woonsocket before. I don't intend to spoil my record for a silly cat."

The woman was crying.

As quick as a cat herself, Louisa climbed to the window ledge. She jumped out onto the driver's shoulders. "Yes, you will wait," she cried. "Don't you see the lady is crying?"

He was dumfounded. He held her with one hand and scratched his head with the other. Then he burst out laughing. He set Louisa down on the ground. "Run along after the cat," he said. "I'll wait a few minutes. Mind you don't chase it into the woods—you'll get lost."

The woman called after Louisa. "I'd better come with you. The cat won't come to you. He's frightened. He never would go to strangers." She scrambled down from the coach.

"Don't worry," Louisa called back. "All animals like me."

Soon she saw the cat hiding in the brush at the side of the road. It crawled farther back toward the woods when she came near. She talked to it softly, then walked right up to it, picked it up, and cradled it in her arms. The woman could scarcely believe her eyes. "He never did that before," she murmured.

They went back and the driver mended the woman's basket. She fastened the cat in firmly. She climbed into the coach.

The driver lifted Louisa up to the step. "How would you like to ride up in front with me?" he asked.

"Oh, I'd love to!" she answered. The driver swung her up onto the high seat.

Horses Are
Like People

LOUISA WISHED Anna and Lizzie could see her. She wished the boys who teased her could see her too. She was so high she could touch the branches of the trees and look down into the birds' nests. She stood up on the seat and stretched her arms out wide in pure enjoyment.

"It feels just like flying," she cried.

The driver pulled her down onto the seat. "You'll have to sit still and hold tight," he said. "You might get dizzy and fall off."

Louisa didn't get dizzy, for she loved to stand on high places. She sat down, though, because the driver was worried.

"What are the horses' names?" she asked.

The driver grinned. He liked to talk about his horses. "That one up in front on this side is Bess," he said. "She's a good puller. She always does more than her share."

"My little sister is named Bess. Only we call her Lizzie."

"The horse next to Bess is Jim. The two back horses are Mars and Bill."

"Do Mars and Bill go in front sometimes?"

"I used to change them around but they work better behind Bess."

"Do you always put Jim next to Bess?"

"I changed Jim around too when I first got him. I nearly sold him one day. He didn't seem to get along with the others. I tried him with Bill. He kicked and bit at Bill. Then I tried him with Mars. He wouldn't work at all with Mars. He just loafed and let Mars do all the pulling. I was disgusted with him. Then, one day, I put

81

him up front with Bess. They got along fine together. Jim worked as hard as Bess. Now he is
one of the best horses I ever had. He and Bess
understand each other."

"I guess horses are like people," said Louisa.

"You're exactly right," agreed the driver.

There were so many things Louisa wanted to
know that the time passed quickly. The driver
was surprised when they came to the first houses
of Woonsocket. The horses began to run.

"We've made a quick trip," the driver said.
"Do you see the inn up ahead?"

Louisa saw a white stone building with a sign
hanging out in front.

"That's where we stop to change horses. This
team's getting tired. They know they get to eat
here, and rest. That's why they're hurrying."

The horses fairly flew. The driver cracked his
whip in the air with a flourish. People ran to
the doors to watch the stagecoach pass. Louisa

waved and shouted. They whirled up to the inn in a cloud of dust.

The driver pulled the horses to a stop. The innkeeper came out. He invited the passengers to come inside to eat and rest awhile. The stable-boys ran out and unhitched the tired horses and led them into the barn at the side of the inn. Then they brought out four fresh horses and backed them up to the coach.

The driver lifted Louisa down. "You can buy your lunch in the inn," he said.

"Mother packed some lunch in a box for me."

"Then you can sit out here and watch them hitch up the fresh horses, if you like."

Louisa liked that. She got a cold drink from a well in front of the inn.

Soon the people began to come out and get into the coach again. The driver sat Louisa in-side this time. He thought she might be ready to take a nap.

Later in the afternoon he stopped the horses at the top of a long hill. They were breathing so hard their sides worked like a bellows. He let them rest awhile, and went around to the door of the coach to see how his little passenger was getting along. She was sitting as still as a mouse. The big cat was on her lap, taking a snooze after his adventure.

"I want to ride outside in the fresh air, please," she said. She put the cat back in his basket and fastened it tightly.

The driver lifted Louisa onto the front seat again. Before they had gone far she knew the names of these horses, too.

It didn't seem long before the afternoon was gone and they came to Providence. The coach rumbled over the cobblestone streets and pulled up at a large inn crowded with people. "We can never find Mother's friend and her husband among all these strangers," Louisa thought.

The driver looked down at the many heads from his high place. Suddenly he touched his cap with his whip. "There they are!" he said, pointing over the crowd. He took Louisa to them. "Here's a little bundle I've brought you from Boston," he said. "I told Mr. Alcott I would see that it arrived safe in your hands."

Mrs. Carleton took Louisa into her arms. "I would know this little girl anywhere!" she cried. "She looks just like her mother."

The driver brought Louisa's trunk. Louisa thanked him for taking such good care of her. He patted her on the head and said, "We'll have another ride together when it's time for you to go home again."

The woman leaned out of the coach and thanked Louisa again for saving her cat.

Everybody waved good-by and the coach rumbled off. Then Louisa went home with Mr. and Mrs. Carleton.

Louisa called the Carletons Auntie and Uncle, though they weren't really related to her. Auntie's house was tall and narrow. It didn't have a front porch. Stone steps led to the front door. Inside was a wide hallway. On one side of the hall was the door to the dining room. On the other side were the doors to the big double parlor and the library.

A wide straight stairway led upstairs from the front door.

When Auntie and Uncle and Louisa entered the front door, a tall boy came running down the stairs to meet them. He was Christopher, Auntie's son. Louisa liked him at once. He shook hands with her as politely as though she were a young lady.

"I'll take your bag upstairs for you," he said. "Would you like to come up? I'll show you where your room is."

Louisa followed him up the wide steps. On the second floor was another hall with more steps going up from it.

"Those stairs go to the third story," said Christopher. "The maid and the cook have their rooms up there. Above that is the attic. I'll take you up someday. You can see all over the city from there."

He led the way to a door at the front of the house. "This is to be your room," he said.

"You mean I'm to have a room all my very own?" It seemed strange to Louisa to have a room by herself.

"Of course," replied Christopher. "Mother has had lots of fun getting it ready for you." He threw the door open.

Louisa was so astonished that she could only stand and stare. In front of her was a great four-poster bed. It was covered with light blue silk that hung from the ceiling to the floor. The bedspread was blue, too, and trimmed with lace ruffles. It looked like a fairy queen's bed.

She looked all around the room with wide eyes. She had never seen anything so lovely. It was all like fairyland to her. On one side of the room was a white marble fireplace. It had shining brass andirons. A bright little copper kettle hung by a crane over the coals in the fireplace. On each end of the mantel was a brass candlestick with pretty dangling crystals. There was a china clock in the middle of the mantel. On one side of it a little china boy bowed to a pretty china girl on the other side.

On a small gold table near her bed was a lamp. The bottom of it was china with pink roses and little blue flowers painted on it. The top half was clear glass. In one corner of the room was a dressing table with a mirror in a gold frame above it. The floor was covered with a thick, flowered carpet.

There were so many pretty things to look at that Louisa thought she never could see them all. Auntie came up to help her unpack and put her clothes away. She was glad that Louisa was so happy about her room.

A tinkling bell sounded from downstairs. "That's the dinner bell," said Auntie. "We'll finish unpacking tomorrow. Come along. You must be hungry.

Louisa was too tired to eat. She went downstairs to the table, but almost before she could see what was on her plate, she was asleep.

"Poor darling," said Auntie.

Uncle gathered her up in his arms and carried her upstairs. She didn't even wake up when Auntie got her ready for bed and tucked her in. Auntie smiled at the innocent, rosy face. She kissed Louisa, then blew out the lamp, and went back downstairs.

New Faces-
New Ways

LOUISA WAS AWAKENED by a crackling sound. At first she thought, "That's Father starting the morning fire. It's time to get up." She opened her eyes, then laughed aloud.

The noise she had heard was the fire in her pretty white fireplace. The maid was laying fresh wood on it. She turned around when she heard Louisa laugh. "So you are awake already?" she asked pleasantly.

"Who are you?" asked Louisa.

"I am Ellen. There's warm water for you in the pitcher. I'll put the tub in front of the fire and place the screen behind it. That will give you a nice, warm place to bathe. It is still chilly in the mornings."

Louisa thought it was funny to go to so much trouble just to wash, but she didn't say anything. Ellen was going to help her dress, too. Louisa had to laugh at that.

"I always dress myself," she said. "Even my little sister Lizzie can dress herself. Anna and I help her sometimes. Mother has many other things to do around the house. She hasn't time to help big girls like Anna and me."

Ellen was glad Louisa could take care of herself. She had much to do. "Breakfast will be ready soon," she said. "Come down when you hear the bell."

Louisa had always been called to breakfast by Mother's cheery voice. She wondered if Mother were calling the girls and Father now to come and eat their hot cereal.

The bell rang. Louisa ran to the stairs. She

saw the smooth banister. "What a wonderful slide it would make!" she thought. In a moment she was astride it. Down she flew! This was the smoothest railing she had ever been on. She came to the end but was going too fast to stop and she landed on the floor with a thump.

Ellen heard her fall and came running. "What happened?" she gasped.

"I slid off the banister."

"*Tch, tch, tch,*" clucked Ellen. "Nice little girls don't slide down banisters. Only tomboys do that. We don't like tomboys in Providence. Come to breakfast now. The others are waiting to be served."

Louisa ran into the dining room. "Good morning, every——"

What she saw on the breakfast table made her stop short. She had never seen so much food at one time. She was used to cereal and nothing more. Here on the table were bacon and eggs, biscuits, marmalade, tea, cocoa, milk, and warm, cooked cereal, also. What a feast!

Ellen served her bacon and eggs. Louisa didn't know what to do. There was something that Auntie had forgotten. The Alcotts were vegetarians. Vegetarians don't eat meat. Louisa had been taught to eat what was set before her, but she couldn't eat the bacon. So she just looked at Auntie. When Auntie saw Louisa looking at her, she remembered.

"Louisa doesn't eat meat, Ellen. Her people are vegetarians, so, while she is here, serve her fruits and vegetables and plenty of bread and milk, but no meat."

Ellen had never heard of vegetarians before. She thought the Alcotts must be queer people. She told Cook about it. Cook wanted to see a child who had never eaten meat. "She must be awful skinny and pale," she thought. She came from the kitchen and peeked through the pantry door at Louisa. She saw a rosy-cheeked, bright-eyed little girl at the table. She was astonished, and shook her head in wonder.

After breakfast Louisa went into the big front parlor. A desk with shelves of books above it stood in one corner. On the desk was a beautiful red quill pen. Louisa could hardly wait to take hold of it.

All morning she thought about the red quill pen. Finally she said, "I think I'd better write a letter to Mother."

Auntie didn't know that Louisa could really write, but she said, "I know your mother will be glad to hear that you are all right. You may use the red quill, if you like."

That, of course, was what Louisa wanted. She sat down to write, but the chair was too low for her. She climbed onto the desk to reach books on the shelves so that she could put a few fat ones in the chair. She had her arms full and was about to jump down, when she tripped on the inkwell. Over she went. Down went the books and Louisa, knocking the quill and inkwell off the desk and spilling ink everywhere.

Auntie heard her fall. So did Ellen and Christopher. All came running. They heard Louisa crying at the top of her voice.

"Oh, dear," thought Auntie, "she's hurt and her visit's just begun." They picked her up.

"It's the quill pen that's hurt, not me," she explained. Ellen didn't say anything, but she looked hard at all the muss she would have to clean up.

Louisa said, "Let me help you wipe up the ink, Ellen."

"The quill's easily mended," said Christopher. He took out his pocketknife and sharpened the quill point so that it was as good as new. Then he put a big dictionary on the chair, and Louisa started again to write her letter.

She began: "Dear Mother, I——" and then the bell rang. Luncheon was ready.

It seemed to Louisa that all she did was eat.

"I wish I could send some of my dessert to Lizzie and Anna," she thought. She fairly stuffed herself to bursting with cake and custard. Funny little Louisa wanted to eat enough at one time to last all summer!

A Doll's Funeral

LUNCHEON WAS OVER. Louisa saw several little girls come down the street carrying dolls. She watched them. "Oh, dear me! They're turning in here!" she thought.

She ran to Auntie, crying, "Are those girls coming to see me? I don't want to play dolls."

"It will be rude of you not to play. They are trying to be friendly with you."

Louisa frowned. "I'll play dolls with them just this one time. Then they'll have to play my way. I won't tell them I haven't a doll. They can think mine's broken."

Auntie let the little callers in and introduced

them to Louisa. As soon as Auntie had gone upstairs, they began to play "grownups" with their dolls.

"How's your little girl this afternoon?" they asked Louisa.

"Oh, I am brokenhearted about her! My child was killed just before I left home the other day," replied Louisa.

"How dreadful!" they cried. "How did it happen, Louisa?"

"She fell out of a tree. She was such a tomboy, always climbing trees, no matter how I scolded. She fell asleep in the treetop. I heard the birds making a fuss, and ran out. There lay my poor Dolly on the ground."

"Dear, dear! Did you have a funeral?"

Louisa hadn't thought of that. "We're having the funeral today," she said quickly. "Will you help me bury her?"

"Yes, indeed we will," they all said eagerly.

100

"First, though, we must hurry home and put on some funeral clothes."

"Maybe Auntie has some that will do. She has an attic."

Auntie said of course she had dress-up things. She sent Ellen up to the attic with the children to open the trunks.

"You can play there all afternoon, if you like," she said.

The girls squealed with delight when they saw what was in the trunks.

"Oh! Ooh! Ooh-ooh! What an elegant funeral we shall have!" they cried.

"May I wear this black skirt, Louisa?" begged one.

"Please let me have the little bonnet."

"Oh my, my! Somebody help me put on this corset, will you, please?"

"Here's a hat with a black veil that will be just right for the mother to wear. And here's a pair

of high, button shoes. They're kind of big, but they will really look nice under that long skirt you have on."

They were all talking at once and were so excited they forgot to act sad. When they were all dressed, though, they became quite sober and talked softly and were very sweet and sympathetic to Louisa about her doll.

They began to plan the funeral. Suddenly Louisa remembered she didn't have a doll to bury. She went to Auntie and whispered her trouble to her. "We can't have a funeral without a doll to bury."

Auntie thought a minute. "I have an old doll head somewhere. We can take a roll of cloth and tie in onto the head and make it look like a body. We'll cover it with lace and no one will guess the difference. You run back to the girls and make the coffin while I find the doll head."

Louisa and the others found a shoe box. They

lined it with white satin that was in the trunk and covered it with velvet.

"It's the most beautiful coffin we ever had," they declared.

Auntie called Louisa downstairs just as they were finishing. She handed her the doll, all fixed up. When Louisa saw it, she burst into tears.

"Why, Louisa, what is the matter? What's wrong with you?"

"She's just so beautiful," Louisa said between great sobs. "I've never seen such a sweet doll. I can't bear to think that she's dead."

Auntie tried to comfort her. "You can have her come alive again tomorrow."

"That doesn't make her alive now. We have to have the funeral, because everything is ready."

When Louisa laid the doll in the coffin, all the girls cried. They sang a sorrowful tune as they carried the coffin down the attic stairs, past the third floor, through the upstairs hall, and down the stairs and front steps. The little procession ended in the back yard near a lilac bush. There they dug a grave and lined it with grass and flowers, and buried Louisa's child. They placed a stone over the top and were about to start crying again when they heard Auntie calling.

They ran to the house to see what she wanted. She had a tea party waiting for them. At sight of the pretty cakes and sandwiches they forgot all about the funeral.

After tea they took off their fancy dresses and put them back in the trunks in the attic.

"We must go home now, Louisa. This has been the best time we have had all year."

"Be sure to come tomorrow," Louisa called after them as they left, "and bring your children." She had forgotten she didn't like dolls.

Early next morning she ran out and dug up Auntie's doll. The night in the ground hadn't seemed to hurt it, but Louisa thought it might have taken cold. She kept it in bed with a mustard plaster for a while.

The little girls came nearly every day. Sometimes they played that their dolls were naughty children who had to be punished, or they had the measles. Other days the dolls became princesses. There was not a dull minute. Louisa had such a good time that she almost forgot her tomboy ways. Then something happened.

Prisoner in
the Attic

IT WAS a dark, rainy afternoon. Louisa's friends couldn't come over to play. She felt cross and grumpy, and went up to her pretty room and leaned on the window sill. She pressed her nose against the windowpane and made faces at the raindrops.

She looked down into the street. Some ragged little children were running about in the rain. They were jumping over mud puddles and having a merry time. Watching them made her homesick. She thought, "At home I can play in the rain too. That's lots more fun than staying in a stuffy old house by myself. I'm tired of being a sissy girl all the time. I'm going outdoors right now and play with those children."

She peeked out into the hall. No one was in sight. Auntie was making calls. Ellen was on the third floor. Cook was out for the afternoon.

Louisa slid down the banisters and skipped out the front door. Soon she was jumping over mud puddles and rolling hoops and having a gay time with the children in the street.

They were playing near a pastry shop. After a while they stopped and looked into the window. The other children stared, fascinated by all the delicious-looking things on display. There were gingerbread boys fastened to pieces of cardboard, jars of peppermint candy, boxes of maple sugar, puddings, pies, and beautiful cakes.

"I'd like that gingerbread," said a little boy.

"I'd like to have that apple pie," said another.

"I could eat everything in the window," cried another little boy.

108

A very small boy began to cry. "I'm hungry," he bawled.

Louisa looked at him. He was pale and thin. "Are you really hungry?"

"Of course he's hungry. We're all of us hungry all the time."

"Oh, how selfish I've been," cried Louisa. "I've had cake and pie and all kinds of good things at Auntie's. I forgot all about sharing with others who are hungry and have no food. Come with me," she told them. "There's plenty of wonderful food at Auntie's. There'll be enough for everybody."

Louisa ran into the house and down to the kitchen. No one was there. She looked into the pantry. No one was there, either. Louisa didn't want to keep the hungry children waiting. She led them into the pantry and opened the cupboards wide. How fine it was that there was plenty of everything! She gave the children potatoes and rice, eggs and flour and bread and meat, and cake and pudding. They couldn't speak, they were all so surprised. Louisa helped the little boy carry his share of the load home. It took her longer than she thought it would.

She skipped all the way back to Auntie's house. "I am happier than I've been any day since I left Mother," she said to herself. "It's because I thought of somebody else. 'It is best to give away the nice things,' Mother always says. Now I know what she means."

She skipped back into Auntie's house as happy as a lark.

Auntie and Cook and Ellen were standing in the front hall. Ellen looked cross. Cook looked angry. Auntie looked stern.

"Louisa, where have you been? Look at your pretty dress. It's all wet and splashed with mud. You know better than to play in the rain. You slipped out without asking permission. You left

the front door open, and see what has happened. Look at the floor! It is tracked with mud from the front door to the kitchen. Tramps came while Cook and I were gone. They stole all the food in the pantry. There isn't a thing left for supper."

"Oh, no," said Louisa, "there weren't any tramps. I gave the food to the children. They were so hungry! Oh, Auntie, their mothers were so happy to get the food! It is just the way it is at home. Fathers are out of work. They haven't money to buy enough for their children to eat. Isn't it wonderful that you had enough to share it with them?"

"Louisa! What are you saying? Did you bring children in here from off the street? Did you give them all of the food from my pantry without asking anyone?"

"They were hungry," said Louisa simply. "You were away."

112

When Louisa saw that Auntie was not pleased, she was surprised. At her home Father and Mother shared everything they had. They laughed and were happy that they had enough to help those who were less fortunate than they.

"I don't know how to punish you for this, Louisa. It was wrong for you to take food from the pantry without asking permission first. You know that, I'm sure."

"We aren't hungry," said Louisa. "It was right to give the food to hungry people."

"Don't talk back, Louisa. I said it was wrong to take food without asking. Now you must go to the attic and stay there until you tell me you're sorry that you did it."

Angry and bewildered because Auntie didn't understand *why* she had given the food away, Louisa rushed up the stairs. *She* couldn't understand why she must be punished for trying to help needy people.

"I'm not sorry," she said to herself. "I'm not sorry." The more she said it the angrier she grew. On the way to the third floor, she stamped her feet on every step. On the way to the attic, she kicked every step. She was acting like a bad-tempered, naughty child.

She banged the attic door behind her as hard as she could. It seemed to shake the house. She locked the door. Then she turned and looked around the attic. It didn't look the same, now that she was up here by herself. It was a great big attic. There were dark shadows under the eaves. The shadows made eerie shapes on the walls.

Louisa went over to one of the low windows and opened it. She leaned out far over the sill.

"Oh, oh, oh! I can see the whole world from here. Down there is the lilac bush where I buried Dolly the other day."

Away off were the fields and the woods.

"There's the road where the stagecoach runs.

There's the inn. The people look like dwarfs. I can almost see Mother's house!"

Then Louisa was quiet for a while. She was thinking. She wondered what everybody was doing at home. The sun was low in the west. Father would be coming home. Anna would be helping Mother with supper. Lizzie would be playing with her dolls. Louisa wondered if she would ever see them again. Auntie had said, "Stay there until you tell me you're sorry."

"I'm not sorry, not one bit. I shall stay up here all night." She saw the lights begin to show in the houses below, and the lamps glimmer one by one as the lamplighter made his rounds. She heard mothers call other children in to supper. No one called Louisa.

"Maybe, if I'm never sorry, I'll live up here always. Maybe I'll be like the old woman in the tower in the fairy tale. Maybe everybody will forget that I'm up here."

115

She began to wish she had not stamped on the stairs. She realized that she had behaved very childishly. Father and Mother would be unhappy when they heard about that.

She wished she were home. "If ever I get home again, I'm going to be more like Anna. I'm going to do my work and not run away and play all day. It was naughty of me to kick the stairs and lose my temper. I am sorry about that but not about the food."

It grew dark in the attic. Louisa leaned on the window sill and looked toward home. She blinked hard to keep from crying. "I shall not cry. If I do, Auntie will think I'm sorry, and I'm not sorry."

All was quiet. The whole city was still. Louisa laid her head on her arms. In a moment she was asleep.

She woke up suddenly. There were voices down below. Auntie, Uncle, Christopher, Ellen, and Cook were all talking. Loudest of all was Christopher.

"Mother, Louisa didn't understand," he said. "She imagined you would be pleased because she thought of the other children. They share everything at her home. She didn't stop to think that the food was not hers."

"Oh, the poor little girl!" said Auntie. "No wonder she felt hurt."

"Run quickly, Christopher," said Uncle. "Go to Louisa and tell her we didn't understand about sharing. Tell her we are sorry."

Ellen said, "Tell her I won't say another word about the muddy floors."

Cook said, "I have a little cake that I had tucked away for myself. I'll bring it to her, and a glass of milk, bless her little heart."

Louisa heard Christopher running up the stairs. She ran to let him in. When he picked her up, she cried and cried. She knew everything

117

was all right, but she cried anyhow. She was sorrier and sorrier that she had acted so ugly coming up the stairs. She told Christopher over and over how sorry she was. Christopher sat down in a little old rocking chair. While he held her in his arms and rocked her, she cried all her naughtiness away. Finally he gave her his big handkerchief, and she wiped her eyes and blew her nose.

Then they went downstairs together. Everybody hugged everybody else and said they were sorry. They all had a little supper in Louisa's room. Then Auntie read to her until she went to sleep.

The next morning the sun was shining and the birds were singing. The little girls came with their dolls and fancy hats and dresses. Louisa forgot all the troubles of the day before.

A week later she went home.

She didn't forget what she had thought out in the attic at Auntie's. She didn't run out to play and leave all her work for Anna any more, but swept and dusted and sewed.

Mother was happy to have such a helpful Louisa. Father was proud of his little girl.

"Louisa has changed," said Mother one day. "She's growing into a lovable child."

"Something happened to her while she was away," said the wise father.

Mother wrote a little note in Louisa's diary and told her how pleased they were with her.

The Alcotts
Move Again

"I LOVE TO MOVE," said Louisa one fine spring day. "Some people I know have lived in the same place for years and years."

"I feel sorry for them," said Anna. "It's so much fun to wake up in a new place."

Anna and Louisa were busy packing while they talked. Lizzie ran back and forth bringing them things to pack.

The Alcotts were moving again. They were leaving Boston. Father could find no school where he could teach. There was no work that he could do in the city.

"We must go where I can plant a garden," he

said. "Then we shall have food even if we have no money. Perhaps I can raise enough produce that I can sell some too."

"I'll be glad to have Louisa off the streets and out of the crowded city. Where shall we go?" asked Mrs. Alcott.

"Come to Concord," a good friend wrote to Mr. Alcott. This friend was a very great man. His name was Ralph Waldo Emerson, and he lived in Concord. "It is a good place for children," he said. "My children are happy here. They can run and play without danger. The air is clean and fresh. There are streams, and fields, and forests, and gardens. Best of all, there are many good people. They make fine neighbors."

Mr. Alcott liked Mr. Emerson. He trusted him and listened to his advice.

So the Alcotts moved to Concord. They lived in a pretty cottage at the edge of the village. They loved it.

Father made a large garden at the side of the house. There was an orchard, too. All about them were rolling meadows and forest land, just as Mr. Emerson had said.

The first morning in Concord, before she was really wide awake, Louisa lay listening to the sounds that came through the open windows. She waited to hear the noise of horses' feet, and the racket of wagon wheels rolling over cobblestones. She waited for the *toot, toot, toot* of the steamboats in Boston Bay. Not one of these old sounds did she hear. That made her open her eyes in surprise. Then she remembered—this was Concord, her new home.

Strange sounds came from outdoors. Roosters were crowing, birds singing.

Louisa hurried and took her morning bath, dressed in a hurry, and ran out to see this new and wonderful country. She sniffed the fresh clean scent of the pine trees.

It seemed to her that the whole world sparkled like a jewel. She loved to see dew shining on the meadows in the early sunlight. She thought she must be dreaming when she saw the pink apple blossoms and the white cherry and plum blooms. She shut her eyes and pinched herself, then looked again. "I'm awake," she said aloud. "It's all really here."

"I believe you like the country," said a kind voice behind her.

Louisa turned around. Who could this be, up as early as she was?

It was Mr. Emerson. Mrs. Emerson was with him. They carried baskets on their arms.

"We've come to have breakfast with you," said Mrs. Emerson. "I know how hard it is to find pots and pans and food after you move, so I brought breakfast with me."

Louisa ran to call Mother. Mother was digging soap and towels out of a barrel and wondering what barrel or box the breakfast food and dishes were in.

"We have company for breakfast, Mother," shouted Louisa happily.

Mother was startled. "Oh, dear!" she thought. "Where can we eat? What can we eat? The tables and chairs are covered with packages and boxes and bags."

Just then Mrs. Emerson came in. "It is so beautiful this morning, Mr. Emerson and I thought we'd like to share our breakfast with you. Can't we eat out under the apple trees? It's really very pleasant outside."

"Let's do! Let's do!" sang Louisa, who could not bear to come into the house so soon and leave the beautiful outdoors.

Mr. Emerson and Mr. Alcott carried the table out into the orchard. Anna and Louisa gathered apple blossoms. Lizzie brought a bowl for them and set it on the table. Mrs. Emerson and

Mother unpacked the baskets and put the food on the table. What a merry breakfast they had!

Louisa looked up into the blossoms overhead and at the happy faces around her, and cried, "Let's live here always!"

BUSY DAYS AT CONCORD

Father worked hard at his own gardening and woodchopping, and he helped near-by farmers in their busy seasons. Sometimes he cut wood for other people and received, in return, the right to cut all the wood he would need at home during the cold season.

Many times the three sisters went with him into the tall pine groves. While he worked, they played in the dry pine tags, sometimes finding Indian pipes and toadstools. When they grew tired, they sat and watched Father swinging his ax, and they talked of all the new and wonderful things they had seen and heard. Anna was always interested, and quiet Lizzie listened, but Louisa was the one most curious—always anxious to see, hear, and do.

The family soon made many new friends. The Emersons brought the Hawthornes, who lived quite near. Mr. Hawthorne wrote books. The Goodwins and the Channings came often, too. These people had children, and their children brought others, so the Alcott girls soon had lots of new playmates.

They had wonderful times in Concord. The Emerson children showed them where the wild strawberries grew, where the violets were thickest, and where the beautiful pink mountain laurel was to be found in the hills. The boys pointed out the best trees to climb, and the best pools to fish in.

Louisa loved the woods and hills around Concord, and she raced like a colt over the slopes of the open country. It was much better for her than the streets of Boston—but sometimes it, too, was not a very safe place for her.

One day a frightened neighbor came running to the Alcott home.

"Mrs. Alcott! Mrs. Alcott!" she called. "Your little Louisa is going to be killed!"

Mother ran to the door, her face full of concern. "What has happened? Where is she?"

"In the top of the sycamore tree at the edge of the cliff." The woman pointed toward the dangerous spot. "There's the tree. Can you see her, or has she already fallen?"

Mrs. Alcott saw Louisa high up against the sky. She looked like a tiny speck so far above the ground. Louisa caught sight of Mother, and took off her sunbonnet and waved.

Mother untied her apron and waved it back.

"Louisa will be all right," she said to the well-meaning neighbor. "She's used to climbing, and the wind and sunlight are good for her. She will be all right."

The neighbor went away shaking her head. She was not so sure.

Mother would not have been so sure, either, if she had heard what the boys were saying. They were at the foot of the tree watching Louisa.

"She's climbing much too high," said Tom. "The branches won't hold her. Doesn't she know any better?"

"I dared her to go to the top," said Cy, "and she'll do it."

"What if it breaks with her? Tell her to come down—and carefully."

Louisa was already at the top. "Look at me! Look at me! I did it!"

Just then there was a loud crack.

"Come down! Come down now! And come slowly!" screamed the boys.

Louisa teased them. She swayed in the creaking treetop until she tired of it. Then she climbed back down, slowly but surely.

"Let's go fishing," suggested Frank, when Louisa was safe on the ground.

"I want to go, too," said Louisa.

"Girls can't fish. They're even afraid of fishing worms."

"I'm not!"

"You'll cry if you hook a fish."

"I won't either. I'm not a crybaby."

"I can make you cry."

"No, you can't."

"I'll show you I can. Come here. Hold out your hands!"

Louisa held her hands outstretched. Suddenly Frank whipped a book strap out of his pocket and lashed it across the backs of them.

Tom and Cy cried in anger and snatched the strap from him. They chased him home, using the strap on him every step of the way.

Louisa followed at their heels. "It didn't hurt. It didn't hurt," she shouted. "Only let me go fishing with you."

It wasn't long before all the boys knew that Louisa couldn't resist a dare. It came to be a kind of game to find something new for her to try.

"I dare you to jump the fence!" cried one.

"I dare you to chew tobacco!" teased another.

"I dare you to rub pepper in your eyes!"

Louisa took every dare. Mother was at her wits' end. Every day Louisa came home bruised, or sick, or nearly blind. "Why *won't* you play with your doll again and forget the boys and their rough play?"

"Dolls aren't exciting. Boys have so much more fun than girls."

A day came, though, when Louisa had to be quiet. She and Cy were playing in the barn. Cy was her favorite playmate, because his dares were always dangerous and she never knew how they were going to come out. Cy climbed into the haymow and walked out across a beam high above the floor. Louisa, balancing easily, followed closely behind him.

"I dare you to drop," he called over his shoulder to her.

Louisa dropped. She was badly shaken up, with both ankles sprained, and had to stay in bed for days and days.

At first the children stopped by every day to visit her. They brought with them all kinds of presents—bouquets of flowers, all kinds of fruit, and even kittens and turtles. After a while, though, they forgot her and did not come often. She became tired and lonely.

Mother felt sorry for the little prisoner who missed her freedom so greatly. One day she brought her a pencil and some paper. "Why don't you write a little story or play for me?" she suggested. "It will help you to pass the time away—and I think it will be fun too."

"Oh, Mother, I'll write out one of the plays Anna and I used to give in the evenings in Boston," said Louisa.

Soon she was scribbling away, and the time passed quickly now.

When the play was finished, Mother and Father read it and thought it was as good as some grownups could write.

"Copy this, Louisa," said Father. "Spell correctly and write it neatly."

Louisa did as he told her.

"Keep on writing," Father told her. "Finish each play or story or poem carefully. Perhaps someday you'll write a real book."

Play Days
at Concord

TIME FLEW BY. The Alcotts were poor and life in their little cottage was quite bare. They cooked in the fireplace because they had no stove. Sometimes they had only two meals a day, because they still shared their food with other families who had less than they.

The children didn't mind being poor. Their house was full of affection and gay spirits and they shared an abundance of family jokes. They were happy, too, because they had the woods and the meadows and the orchard to play in.

In the long winter evenings, after Father had taught them their lessons, he read to them from Dickens' tales and their old favorite, *Pilgrim's Progress*.

One of their best-loved pastimes was the weekly pillow fight which they were allowed to have just before going to bed. They were lively battles and the girls loved them. They jumped and ran around in their nightgowns, throwing pillows at one another. Sometimes, in their enthusiasm and energy, they collided and fell in a tangled heap of arms, legs, and rumpled pillows.

Finally, when they were all breathless, they put the pillows back in place on their beds. After such romps they dropped off to sleep as soon as their heads touched the pillows.

Behind the Alcott cottage was a fine, big barn. The girls used it for their playhouse. They could do just as they pleased there, and not bother anybody.

"This will be just the place to give our plays in," said Louisa. She climbed up into the loft.

"We can act out *Jack and the Beanstalk!*" she shouted. "The giant can fall out of the hayloft."

"Oh, what fun!" cried Anna. "Jack can climb up the ladder to the giant's castle and steal the goose that lays the golden egg."

"We can cover the ladder with a vine, so it will look like a beanstalk. Let's get to work on it right away."

They swept out the barn and moved everything out of the way. Some of their friends came in to play. Louisa set them to work. The boys dragged in part of an old chicken house, and Louisa had them paint it. They propped it up with the bran box. "Now it looks like the cottage that Jack and his mother lived in," they said.

"We need a long vine to cover up the ladder. Is there a wild grapevine somewhere near here?" asked Louisa.

"A grapevine won't look like a beanstalk," the boys said.

136

"I know what we can use. We'll get a squash vine. It grows long and trailing."

"Hurrah!" cried the boys. "We know where to get plenty. They grow along the fences everywhere around here."

"Be sure to ask first," said Anna, "and don't leave any squashes on the vine. That would give the whole thing away."

"A squash would be an awfully big bean, wouldn't it?" someone joked.

Before the children could work more on the play, it was suppertime. They decided not to tell their parents.

"It will be a surprise," they said.

Louisa was so full of plans for the next day that she didn't know what she was doing that evening. After the dishes were washed, she put her pencil and slate in the cupboard and carried the bread and butter into the living room. She emptied the sugar bowl into the salt box.

137

"You need a guardian," Anna said with a giggle. "You must be more careful or Mother will suspect something."

That evening, to please Louisa, Father read the story about the old woman who had three wishes. Anna and Louisa knew it by heart. He came to the part where the old woman wishes the pudding were on the end of her husband's nose.

Louisa cried out, "We can act that out easily. We'll let the pudding down on a string from above in the hayloft."

"Louisa!" shrieked Anna. "You're telling!"

Louisa clapped her hand over her mouth.

Mother and Father didn't seem to notice.

The children of the neighborhood were as busy as bees the next few days. They made the costumes for the play in the barn, so the grown-ups wouldn't guess what was going on.

Louisa was the giant. She wore one of Father's old coats. They had stuffed it with padding from a carriage cushion. She practiced falling out of the hayloft. She fell "ker-spling, ker-splung."

The boys and girls shouted and clapped their hands. "That will be the funniest part of the play," they said.

Finally everything was ready. All the children wrote invitations to their parents. "Come to the Alcotts' barn at four o'clock today," they said.

The mothers of the neighborhood hurried through their work. The fathers came home early. All of them went to the barn.

Little Lizzie met them at the door. She led them to their seats—boards laid across saw horses. A curtain hung down from the rafters at one end of the barn. It was made of many old coverlets sewed together. Nearly every family recognized parts of it.

The curtain went up. There was a loud thud. The curtain came down. The parents heard

140

scurrying feet. The chicken house had fallen down. The boys raised it up and two of them stood behind it and held it up during the performance.

Then the curtain went up again. Everything worked all right this time. The squash vine looked like a beanstalk at the side of the house. Jack climbed up it. He came scrambling down with a squawking hen under one arm.

Something happened then that Jack wasn't expecting. The hen chose that moment to lay a real egg. Everybody laughed. "I thought she was supposed to lay *golden* eggs," someone said.

The play went on. Jack chopped down the beanstalk. Down tumbled Mr. Giant, *bumpety-bump,* and the play was over.

The parents clapped and clapped. They waited to see if the giant were really killed. Then the young actors came back and made their bows.

The fathers and mothers were so well pleased

141

that they said, "Give more plays! We like them very much!"

All summer and fall Anna and Louisa were busy with their plays. Louisa wrote them and Anna helped with the costumes. All the children helped make the scenery and took parts in the plays. Once they acted out the beautiful story of Cinderella. Louisa made a great big pumpkin cariage in which Cinderella rode away.

No wonder Louisa and Anna didn't notice how poor they were! They were so busy with their own projects that they didn't even see how hard Father and Mother were working.

A Plan
and a Move

THE FOURTH of July was an exciting day in Concord. It started at sunrise when there was a six-gun salute. The day soon became very hot. That did not hinder the Light Infantry bugle, drum, and fife corps from striking up lively airs.

The Alcott sisters skipped along the streets, watching the wagons and carriages arriving in town for the parade. The stagecoaches brought in many visitors.

Vendors darted busily through the crowds, selling molasses candy, maple sugar bars, popcorn balls, and apples-on-a-stick.

Finally the parade began. A great cheer arose from the villagers as a log cabin was drawn along by oxen. A man dressed as Uncle Sam strode by, smiling broadly. Then there was a barrel of cider, which was rolled along on wheels. The band marched smartly by.

Everybody was waving a flag, or a banner, which said, "Tippecanoe and Tyler." When a group started singing "The Old Oaken Bucket," the girls joined in with great enthusiasm. The drum corps made lively, stirring music.

That summer a baby girl was born in the Alcott cottage. They named her Abba May. She was like a live doll, with golden hair and pink cheeks. The family adored her.

The cottage was even more crowded now. Anna, Lizzie, and Louisa all slept in one room. It was fun to share their fun and secrets, but Louisa wanted a room of her own now. She liked to write her plays and stories at night, but she couldn't do that now, because Anna and Lizzie couldn't go to sleep with the lamp still burning. In the daytime it was almost impossible to write when they were so many people around and so many things to be done.

Mother was busy with the baby and with endless household duties. Anna and Louisa had to help with the cooking and ironing and sewing. They were up with the crowing roosters, and, after their meager breakfast porridge, they met with Father for an hour's study. Then they did their assigned tasks as fast as possible so they could go outside and play.

Each one of the sisters had her favorite neighborhood playmate. Anna and Lizzie and their chums generally played with their homemade rag dolls.

Louisa liked Cy best of all. They especially loved to race over the grassy meadows and down to the river. She was not happy at all if she could

not beat him in their races and games at least half the time.

Later on, word came that Grandfather May was very ill. Mother took the baby with her to Boston so she could be near him. The three sisters kept the house in order for Father. One night he made a new dish for them—toasted bread dipped in warm water. After supper he told them a fable and read from *Pilgrim's Progress*.

One day Louisa wrote her first letter to her mother. She was proud that she didn't have even one blot in it. In the letter she said, "I'm glad Grandpa is getting better. Please come home soon. We all miss you and our darling Abba May."

After she wrote her letter, she ran down the road to tell Miss Russell about it. Miss Russell was visiting the Emersons and she was glad to help Louisa with her lessons. Almost every day

Louisa walked over to the big, square, frame house of the Emersons.

Miss Russell had already shown her the birdhouse on the barn, the orchard, the flower garden, the chickens, dog, and cat with her litter of kittens. Sometimes she took Louisa inside the house, and the little girl gazed in amazement at the many beautiful and unusual things there. The thing that aroused her curiosity most was the leather buckets.

Sometimes she saw thin, tall, and stoop-shouldered Mr. Emerson sitting in his library, writing. She kept as quiet as possible so she would not disturb him.

Louisa made another friend, Mr. Henry Thoreau. He had bushy eyebrows over deep-set eyes. He was friendly to everyone and quite often he was followed by a swarm of eager children. Starting from the Common, they ended, perhaps, at Hubbard's Grove or Bear Garden Hill. Or

148

he took them up Blue Hill or to Becky Stowe's swampy hole for blueberries.

Mr. Thoreau always made a box of birch bark to hold lichen or berries. As they walked, he told them about all the birds and flowers and trees—how the tanager was the bird which set the woods afire with its brilliant color, how the cobweb was a handkerchief dropped by a fairy, how he could bring down a flock of birds with his call instead of a gun.

Other times Mr. Thoreau took some of the children out on the river in his boat, the blue and green "Musketaquid." Floating smoothly over the still water he pointed out cardinal flowers like flames along the banks, tangled vines among the trees, and the sweet-smelling white pond lilies.

The winter was a busy one, with the usual lessons, household tasks, and games. Father worked hard at anything he could find to do, but they were still very poor. Before they realized it, spring had come.

Then, in May, Father received an invitation to come to England to visit a Temple school which had been named after him. There was a flurry of preparation to make him ready for the trip, and on May 8 Father, with his trunk, a basket of apples, and Mr. Emerson's "Essays," left on the ship "Rosalind" for London.

While Father was gone Louisa did the heavy chores about the house. She carried the buckets of water from the well, and filled the wood-box, and tended the garden. She was quite strong now, and big for her age, and liked the hard work much better than the sewing and ironing. She seemed to thrive on the harder chores.

Mother taught the girls and read to them as Father had always done. Father wrote interesting letters to his family, telling them about London and the many people he was meeting.

Among them was Thomas Carlyle, a writer who was quite famous.

When Father came home, he brought some strangers with him, Mr. Wright and Mr. Lane and his son. The cottage was already so full that Louisa said, "I don't see where we're going to put everybody." Mother managed somehow. She always did.

Nothing was the same in the cottage after Mr. Lane came. He and Father talked together all the time, or went to Mr. Emerson's and talked. Many strange people came to visit. They stayed on, and so the cottage was still more crowded, and Mother and the girls cooked day and night to prepare enough food for all of them.

Everybody talked a great deal. It was very tiresome.

"Why don't you read to us any more, Father? Why don't you send these queer people away?" asked Louisa one day.

"They are not queer, Louisa. They are great thinkers and teachers."

"What do you talk about all the time?"

"Mr. Lane and I wish to try out a wonderful plan. These others are interested, too. They may try it with us."

"What is the plan?"

"It's about a new way of living. You know how poor everyone is, and that there is no work in the cities. Our plan is to go to the country. As a group we shall buy a big farm and live without cities. We shall do everything with our own hands."

"Where will we get goods to make our clothes? Where will you get a plow? Where will sugar come from?"

"We shall raise flax. Linen comes from flax. We'll make our clothes from that. I shall make my own plow. And sugar comes from sugar cane, as you know."

152

"Will the farm have a house large enough for all of us?"

"Yes, a great big house."

"Then I'm ready to go," said Louisa. "I'm tired of this crowded cottage."

"I don't want to leave Concord," said Anna. "This has been the best home we've had in our whole lives."

"I shall miss the barn and all our friends, too," said Louisa, "but I want more room."

It was a long, cold New England winter. Their little house was not very weather-tight, and it took a great deal of wood to keep it warm.

One windy, snowy night the freezing air seeped in at all the cracks in the little cottage. The house was bitter cold. There was practically no wood in the shed. Mother was almost frantic with worry that the family would freeze and become ill from being in a cold house overnight.

Suddenly there was a knock at the door. When

she answered it, she saw a neighbor standing there, smiling. He said he had thought they might be needing some wood so he had brought over a load for them.

Mother was relieved and happy and very grateful. Soon the fireplace had a roaring hot fire which gradually warmed the small house.

Later, Father came in out of the storm, smiling and pleased. He said a poor man who had a sick child at home had asked if he could borrow some wood. So Father had told the man to take all the wood he needed—and had even helped him to wheel it home!

By this time Mother was feeling desperate. She reminded Father that they too had a small baby and their house could be freezing cold by morning.

She was interrupted by a knock at the door. It was a second neighbor who, thinking they might be low on fuel, had brought them a supply of wood. So the fire was piled high again and soon the little house was full of warmth and cheer.

Spring had come before the plan was worked out. Finally Father and Mr. Lane and a few teachers were ready to try it. They bought a farm. It had a big, empty house on it. "It is old, but I can fix it up," said Father.

Many people made fun of the plan. "It won't work," they said.

"Father can do anything," said Louisa. "He can make the plan work."

"Be ready to start in a few days," he said at last. Once more the Alcotts were moving.

DREARY JOURNEY

Moving day came. Louisa stood in the door of the cottage at Concord and looked out. It was early morning.

"It's raining cats and dogs," she told Anna.

"I suppose it will keep on all day," said Anna. "It will be cold riding in the open wagon."

"Who minds a little cold water?" scoffed Louisa. "We must see that Mother and Baby are warm. The rest of us will be all right."

Anna hoped that Father would put off moving. She hoped the wagon wouldn't come. The wagon came, though. All their belongings were piled into it.

There was only one umbrella. Mother took Abba May on her lap and held the umbrella over her. The furniture and food were covered with heavy canvas. The men held heavy brown wrapping paper over their heads and shoulders.

Louisa liked starting off in the rain. "It makes it more exciting," she said. "This is an adventure." She put her arms around Anna to warm her. "We'll crawl under the canvas," she said. "That will keep us dry."

156

"Let's talk about when we grow up," said Anna. "I'm going to be a great actress."

"I shall write plays and act them," said Louisa. "I'm going to make a lot of money."

"Then Father can have a fine pair of boots and a warm coat."

"And Mother won't have to ride in the cold and wet," added Louisa. "Oh, it seems such a long time to wait to grow up. I wish we were rich right now!"

All day long they traveled. The wagon jolted along the muddy, hilly road. The rain came down in torrents. Even Louisa was cold and wet and tired.

It was nearly dusk when the horses turned up a steep hill. Father came running to the side of the wagon. He had walked all the way.

"We're here!" he shouted. "We're here! Everybody get out!"

Anna and Louisa tumbled out from under the

canvas. They saw a big, deserted old farmhouse. The wagon stopped at the door. Just then the sun came out. A great rainbow spread across the eastern sky. Louisa stood up in the wagon. She looked out over the hills and valleys.

"What a wonderful place to play in!" she thought.

Fruitlands

THE NEW HOME was called Fruitlands. The house looked lonely and dirty the night they moved in. It was different in a few days. Mother had it clean and shining. Pretty rugs were on the floor, bright flowers on the table, and a cheery fire burned in the fireplace.

Anna and Louisa soon realized that this was not an ordinary way of living and that they had an actual part in it. They did their share of the work. Anna could bake bread. She and Louisa could prepare a meal for their huge household. They helped Mother with the washing.

Living on a farm had many new and exciting

experiences for them. Daily they watched the growing seeds turn the fields into rows of green. They gathered blueberries and blackberries. They watched the water splash over the big mill wheel. Sometimes they helped rake the hay and carry it to the waiting wagons.

At the end of every day they wrote in their diaries before they went to bed in their small room under the roof.

There was little time for play at Fruitlands. These people believed that no person should possess anything, but that everything must be owned and shared with the others. They believed that animals must not be used for food or made to work for man. That meant that all the food had to be raised on the farm. Nothing was bought at a grocery. The men had to work in the fields. Father worked from dawn to dark. Mother baked from morning till night. It took a lot of bread to feed all the teachers and children.

Father came in late from the fields one night. He was tired and discouraged. "The corn is ready to husk, but we haven't enough workers," he said.

"Then the girls and I shall help," said Mother. "Tomorrow, you will have three new helpers."

The next morning Mother flew around. "The housework must be done before noon," she said, "for we will start husking after dinner."

Anna and Louisa helped Mother instead of having their lessons. This pleased them. Mr. Lane was their teacher at Fruitlands, and they didn't like him.

After dinner they hurried to the barn. Father showed them how to strip the husks off the ears.

Everybody went to work—the teachers, Father, Mother, and the children. It was hard work. Anna's and Louisa's hands were stiff and sore. Their backs ached, but they worked on.

"It will soon be suppertime," said Mother.

161

"Shall we bring the supper out here to the barn so we won't lose any time?"

"Yes, yes," voted everybody. One of the men carried the big iron kettle from the house. It was full of hot, savory vegetable soup. Anna and Louisa brought the loaves of bread that Mother had baked. Father hung up lanterns, so that they could see to eat. The lanterns threw a pretty light on the piles of golden corn.

After supper Mother took Lizzie and Abba May to bed. Anna and Louisa were allowed to stay and husk as long as they could keep awake.

The sun went down. The stars came out. Father built a fire outside the barn. They sat around the fire and went on working. Someone began a song. Everybody joined in. They sang as they worked, all the rest of the evening, until the last ear of corn was husked.

Anna and Louisa were so sleepy that they fairly tumbled into bed.

The moon shone in on Louisa late in the night. It woke her up. She thought about the corn husking.

"That is the best time we have had since we came to Fruitlands."

BARLEY AND THE STORM

"I am going for a good, long run," said Louisa. It was a bright, frosty morning. The Alcotts had been at Fruitlands several months. "Mr. Lane and Father are away, so we won't have any lessons today."

Louisa had long arms and legs. She still thought that running was one of the most enjoyable things in life. On this morning she ran over the hills up to the highest point. From there she could see the beautiful countryside stretching away for miles around. Sometimes she would stretch out under the pine trees there to rest and think and dream. It was almost always quiet, peaceful, and restful.

Today it was different. The wind roared through the branches. In the valley it was warm. On the hilltop it was too cold for Louisa. She ran back down the long slope to the farmhouse as fast as she could go.

"Mother, it's turning cold."

Mother went out to the brow of the hill. She looked worried. There were dark clouds gathering in the north.

"If it snows, the barley will be lost," she said. "It has been cut, but not gathered."

The wind blew colder. The clouds shut out the sun completely.

"Children," she called, "there's not a moment to lose. We must gather in the grain. The men will not return in time."

"How can we, Mother? We haven't a wagon or anything to put it in."

164

"We'll do the way the women did in Bible times. They carried the grain in their aprons. I'll give each of you one of mine."

They all tied on the big aprons, even little Lizzie. Hers dragged on the ground, so Mother fastened it around her neck. Then Mother brought out her biggest sheets. They were of very heavy linen and had been made in Russia. She spread them on the ground.

"Fill your aprons with the barley as fast as you can," she ordered her little army. "Then empty them into the sheets. When the sheets are full, drag them to the barn and empty the grain on the floor, then come back for more. Hurry, hurry, hurry!"

They worked as hard and fast as they could. The wind blew colder. The clouds were black. Slowly the pile of grain grew on the barn floor. The children's feet were bleeding. The sharp stubble cut through their shoes. Their arms ached. Their legs seemed made of wood, they were so tired.

"Keep on a little longer, my brave soldiers," encouraged Mother. "We are nearly finished."

All of them together dragged the last sheet into the barn. The storm came with a fury. It was a blizzard. They ran for the house. They couldn't see in the blinding snow. The wind sucked their breath away.

Mother carried Lizzie so she wouldn't be lost. "Hold onto my apron strings," she called to Anna and Louisa. "It is very easy to lose your way in a storm like this."

They reached the house safely. Mother built up the fire. She bathed the children's feet and wrapped them in soft linen.

"Father will be proud of you," she said, while she worked. "You have saved the barley crop for the winter."

Father came home the next morning. He had

traveled all night. He saw the fields covered with snow and said sadly, "We shall have to go back to the city. There will be no food here. The barley is buried in snow."

Mother said, "Come with me to the barn." Seeing the barley safely harvested, he looked at her in wonder. "How did you do it?" he asked.

She told him all that had happened.

He went back to the house and called the children to him. He put his arms around them and said a little prayer. He thanked God that his children were safe, and thanked Him for their brave and wonderful mother.

Farewell to
Fruitlands

THE WINTER was long and cold at Fruitlands. Mr. Lane was discouraged about their plan. He didn't like the cold and grew tired of the plain food. One morning he went away and didn't come back. He took his son with him. The other teachers also left, one by one.

Anna and Louisa were glad. "I like to have just our family here," Louisa said. "I wish we could always have just us."

Father lost hope and was very sad. "We cannot make the great plan work if people run away when they become discouraged," he said. He worried so much about it that he grew ill. He couldn't eat. Finally he was so weak that he had to go to bed.

One night Mother came to the bed where Anna and Louisa were sleeping. "Wake up!" she whispered. "Get up and dress. Don't make any noise. We mustn't disturb your father. Come to the barn where we can talk."

They dressed as quickly as their shaking hands would let them. They tiptoed out of the house and ran to the barn.

"What is it, Mother? What's the matter?"

"We must leave Fruitlands at once," she said. "I have been through the grain box and the flour bin and the apple cellar. There's not enough food for another day.

"Father is not well enough to travel, but we shall starve if we stay. Louisa, get out the bobsled that Father made in Concord. Nail longer boards onto it. We shall use it like a sleigh. Anna and I will make it soft with pillows and blankets. The three of us can lift Father onto it. We shall pull Father on the sled to our nearest friends', the Lovejoys. We must start as soon as we can, for it feels like rain. If it rains, the snow will melt. Then we couldn't move, for the sled would be too heavy, and the roads would be too soft for a wagon."

A little before daylight they were ready. Louisa made the sled into a sleigh. Then she rubbed soap on the runners and they brought it to Father's bedside. "The soap will make it slide over the floor more easily. We can lift Father onto it here," said Louisa.

Mother and Anna piled the sled with warm blankets. It was no trouble to lift Father, he had grown so thin. Then each took up a small bundle, and they were ready to move. They put Lizzie and Abba May in the sleigh, too.

It was a heavy load and they pulled it a long way. They were very tired, and it began to rain.

"It's the same sort of rain we started to Fruit-lands in," said Louisa, "but everything else is different. Father's sick. Our dear, brave mother looks old and tired. I'm different, too."

Anna began to cry. "You sound so sad."

"I'm not sad, Anna. I'm just growing up. I'm not twelve yet, but I feel old. I'm going to try with all my might to take care of my family. Someday I'm going to make you all rich and comfortable."

"You're always saying that," said Anna.

"I'm always dreaming about it, too."

It was getting harder and harder to pull the sled. Then Louisa saw the Lovejoys' house through the rain.

They hurried as fast as they could and finally reached the Lovejoy house.

Mr. Lovejoy saw them coming. He threw open the door. People ran out, calling, "Wel-come, welcome." They carried Father into the

house. They made a place for Mother by the fire, and brought heaping plates of food to all the family.

How good it was to be among friends again!

ANNA AND LOUISA GO TO WORK

It was a long time before the Alcott family had a home of their own again. They had no money, and for a long time Father was much too weak to work.

The Lovejoys let the Alcotts have three rooms and a kitchen. In the warm, friendly atmosphere Father slowly regained his spirits and strength. He chopped wood to earn some money and at night wrote the story of the undertaking at Fruitlands.

"It is dreadful to be poor," whispered Anna to Louisa one night. "People are talking about our father. They laugh at him behind his back and say, 'That queer Mr. Alcott and his big ideas!' I can't bear it, Louisa!"

"We must find a way to make money," said Louisa. "If we were rich, people would believe in Father."

"How can *we* make money? We're only little girls, Louisa."

"Mr. Emerson will help us," said Louisa suddenly. "We can teach his little children the way Father taught us. He knows what a great man our father is.

"We could have a school for younger children in Mr. Emerson's barn."

"We can help Mrs. Emerson with her sewing, too. I can sew well," added Anna proudly.

The two girls went to the Emersons' the first thing the next morning. They told them all about their plans.

"This is splendid," said Mr. Emerson. "You may begin at once."

175

"I need Anna to help with my sewing today," said Mrs. Emerson. "If Louisa will teach our younger children and the Goodwins' and Channings' each morning, the mothers will be glad to pay her every week."

So Louisa and Anna went to work. They didn't earn enough to rent a house, but they were busy and much happier.

In the afternoons they took care of Lizzie and Abba May. Anna made Lizzie's dolls new dresses from scraps Mrs. Emerson gave her. Louisa made them fancy hats.

"Why, Louisa, those are the most stylish hats I ever saw. I didn't know you could do anything like that," said Anna.

"I didn't, either," replied Louisa.

Lizzie's little playmates saw the hats. "Please make us some, Louisa. We'll pay for them."

"Why, that will be fun. It seems odd to be paid for having fun." Louisa made them many hats, but they wanted more and more of them. She printed a little sign and put it in the window—

DOLL HATS MADE TO ORDER.

It wasn't long before she had more orders than she could fill. She had a hard time finding enough material.

"Make one for me with feathers on it," said one little girl.

"I haven't any more feathers," said Louisa.

The child was unhappy. "I did so want one like Lizzie's."

Another little girl said, "I did, too. It would look so elegant with my doll's new dress."

"Then I must get some more feathers," said Louisa. She went up and down the streets. The children followed her. She came to a back yard where there were chickens. She pointed at them. "There are some feathers," she said.

"How can you get them?" The girls were disappointed.

"I'll show you," said Louisa. She jumped over the fence into the chicken lot. She grabbed at a red hen. The hen was fat and she waddled. She couldn't run fast. Louisa caught her easily and pulled out some of her downy feathers. What a fuss the hen made!

"Those feathers will make very fashionable hats," cried the girls joyously.

"I wish you could get some white feathers for my doll's hat," said one. "They would look so nice with her white satin cloak."

"Perhaps we can find some white hens," said Louisa.

They all ran up and down the streets till they found some white hens. Louisa chased them and pulled feathers with both hands. The little girls stood on the outside of the fence screaming, "Get me one out of that hen. Get me one, get me one!" The hens inside the fence set up a loud squawking.

178

People ran out of their houses to see what was going on. They thought, "Chicken thieves must be after our hens." When they saw Louisa climbing over their fences, chasing roosters and hens, and pulling out their tail feathers, they grabbed their brooms and started after her.

"Who is that dreadful child?" they shouted. They threw sticks at her.

Louisa and the other girls ran home as fast as they could go. They slipped into the house as quiet as mice, and spent the rest of the day making hats.

The summer passed quickly.

"We still haven't enough money," Louisa said with a sigh one night. She and Anna had been counting up their earnings for the summer. "I did so want to buy Mother a new dress and a warm shawl."

"I wish there were some way we could help Mother," said Anna earnestly. "It must be

179

very hard for her to have to live in other people's houses."

"We must keep 'working and hoping.' That is what she tells us to do. Perhaps, someday, times will be better."

HILLSIDE

After a few months they held a family council and decided to go to Boston to try to make a living.

In Boston, Father tried several ways to earn money. Mother took in boarders. As a family they were all unhappy, though. They longed for the peace and quiet of a smaller place. Their life in Concord had spoiled them for living in the city.

With the money which had been left her by her father, Mother bought a house back at Concord. It was a large frame building, with its gate opening onto the highroad over which Paul Revere had galloped on his famous ride to Lexington. Over the hill to the rear a company of redcoats had marched to take part in the first battle of the Revolution.

The house was old and rundown, but Father made a beautiful home of it. How happy Anna and Louisa were! They scoured and cleaned the old walls and floors. They papered and painted and polished.

Outside, there were barns, sheds, and a workshop. Father cut the shop in two and attached a half to each end of the house. One of these wings had big windows and a door opening into the garden.

Mother put a nice desk and comfortable chairs in the room. She made bright-colored rugs for the floor and white ruffled curtains for the windows. In the closet and dresser drawers she hid sweet-smelling herbs.

"This is the sweetest room that ever was," said Louisa, when everything was finished.

"We are glad you like it," said Father and Mother, smiling, "for it is yours, Louisa."

"Mine!" gasped Louisa. "I've wanted a room like this all my life!"

"You have been patient and kind, and have worked hard. You have earned this room. You will enjoy it more now that you deserve it."

"Surely I shall never be unhappy again," cried Louisa. "I can write plays and stories whenever I wish."

FIRST PLAY

Louisa soon wrote a play in her new room. It was a romantic drama, with a beautiful heroine rescued from a dungeon by the noble Duke Roderigo. All the characters in the play were enacted by the four Alcott sisters—from the

182

hero (who, of course, was Louisa, wearing a slashed doublet, bright sash, and tall boots) to the servant who brought in the poison cup. She not only wrote and acted, but she designed the costumes and was stage manager.

The performance was a great success and the audience clapped their hands wildly as the curtain fell.

Louisa was proud and encouraged with her first successful play and she worked in her little room, writing more and more plays and stories. Sometimes she wondered whether she might become an actress, or a playwright, or an author. No matter what she might be, she made up her mind that she would one day give her family the many things they needed and deserved.

Louisa
the Writer

YEARS PASSED. Anna and Louisa were young ladies, beautiful and popular. They were asked to all the gay parties and balls, but they didn't go. They didn't have anything to wear, and they were too busy. The Alcotts were poor again. Father and Mother both worked. Anna and Louisa taught school in the winter and took positions as governesses during the summer. Still there wasn't enough money for party dresses and good times. Lizzie and Abba May were growing up. They needed shoes and clothes.

"I don't know what is going to become of us," Anna said with a sigh. "All we do is work. I would love to have a little fun like other girls before I grow old."

"Don't give up hope," said Louisa, with an encouraging laugh. "I still think that I shall make our fortunes."

Anna smiled sadly. She had heard this before.

Then one day Louisa said, "I am going to Boston. I know that I can make money by writing if I only dare to try."

Mother and Father said, "We believe you are right, Louisa."

Father went up to the attic and brought down Louisa's little old, worn trunk. It was the same trunk that had gone with her to Providence when she was a little girl. Mother and Anna mended and cleaned and pressed Louisa's shabby clothes and folded them neatly into the trunk. Louisa put her pencils and paper and most all of her books into it, too.

Lizzie tucked in a shawl that she had knitted

herself. "You can wear this on cold nights when you are writing," she said.

Abba May gave her some pictures. "Here are some sketches I drew. I shall illustrate your books for you," she promised.

The day came for Louisa to leave. The drayman called for her trunk. Louisa set out for the station. At the corner she turned and waved to Father and Mother and Anna and Lizzie and Abba May.

The townspeople shook their heads. "What are the Alcotts thinking of—sending a young lady alone to the city!" "I'd rather see my daughter dead and in her grave," said one. "She'll come running back soon enough," said another. "Whoever heard of a girl making a living by writing!"

Louisa didn't make her living by writing, at first. She sewed for friends and relatives in Boston. Hour after hour she hemmed sheets and blankets and pillow slips. Day after day she sewed ruffles on ball dresses for other young ladies. While she sewed, she planned her stories, and at night she wrote them.

Finally her stories began to sell. People stopped at bookstores and inquired, "Have you more stories by Louisa May Alcott?" "Do you have a book by Miss Alcott?"

When they passed her on the street, people turned to look at her. "There goes Miss Alcott, the author. Isn't she interesting? Isn't she charming?" they said in admiration.

Then the Civil War broke out. "We need nurses! We need nurses!" came the cry from the battle fronts. "The wounded are dying like flies because there is no one to care for them."

Louisa left Boston and went back home to Father and Mother. "There are no sons to go to war in our family," she said, "but I am young and strong and would make a good nurse. I know that brave young men are dying and that I might save them. I feel I must go."

"Go, and Godspeed," said Father and Mother.

Again Louisa set out alone. Again the people shook their heads. "Is it true that Louisa is going to serve as a nurse? How can the Alcotts let their daughter go into such danger? The hospitals are full of every kind of disease. They are filthy and overcrowded. She is most certainly going to her death."

The hospitals were even worse than Louisa had heard. When she saw the dirty beds and floors, and the poor, unwashed soldiers, she called for buckets of water. She scrubbed and scoured and cleaned. She helped the doctors as they labored over the wounded. She cheered the sick and comforted the dying. People began to hear about her—"Brave, strong, cheerful Louisa Alcott."

Then one night Father received a telegram.

188

Louisa was very ill. They thought she was dying. She had worked too hard without rest and good food and fresh air.

Father went to the hospital and brought her home. She didn't know anybody, not even Father or Mother. She was ill a long, long time, but she didn't die. She finally recovered and began to write again.

She wrote a book that she called *Little Women*. It was about her own family. "Maybe there are other people who have had the same kinds of troubles we have had," she thought. "Maybe there is another little tomboy like me someplace, who will like to hear about the scrapes I got into when I was little. Who knows but that the book may help her?"

An invalid friend took her to Europe as her companion soon after the book was finished. She was gone several months. When the ship that brought her home pulled up to the dock in New York, she saw the great crowds of people. They were all cheering. Bands were playing. "There must be some famous person on this boat," she said to herself. "It is strange that I didn't hear of it." She saw Father waiting for her, but there was such a throng about her that she couldn't get to him.

All at once she heard people shouting her name. Young people were handing open books to her, saying, "Won't you autograph my book, Miss Alcott? "Will you please write your name in mine, Miss Alcott!"

Louisa looked about her in astonishment. She took one of the books and turned it over to see what it was. It was a copy of *Little Women*. Louisa was the famous person everyone had come to see!

Louisa followed her successful *Little Women* with *Little Men,* then *Jo's Boys*. Her health was not good and she took a cottage near Princeton, Massachusetts. There she found rest and quiet, and freedom from the gaze of celebrity seekers. From her window she could see Fruitlands and other familiar scenes of her girlhood.

Never again did the Alcotts have to worry about the rent, or clothes, or food or doctor bills. Louisa's books were read all over the world. She was rich. She bought her family everything that

191

their hearts could desire. Money and fame did not change her. She shared with others all the good things of her life. The lessons she had learned as a little girl were not forgotten.

After a lengthy illness Louisa Alcott died, in 1888. She did not know that her father had died only two days before. She *did* know, however, that she had gained from life the one thing she had always wanted most—to take care of her beloved family.

More About This Book

WHEN LOUISA MAY ALCOTT LIVED

1832   LOUISA MAY ALCOTT WAS BORN IN GERMANTOWN, PENNSYLVANIA, NOVEMBER 29.

There were twenty-four states in the Union.

Andrew Jackson was President.

The population of the country was about 13,706,600.

1834   THE ALCOTT FAMILY MOVED TO BOSTON.

American settlers reached Oregon, 1836.

Samuel Morse made the first daguerrotype portraits in America, 1839.

John William Draper took the first photograph of the moon, 1840.

1843   THE ALCOTT FAMILY MOVED TO FRUITLANDS.

Elias Howe invented the sewing machine, 1846.

The Mexican War was fought, 1846-1848.

The Mormons reached Great Salt Lake, 1847.

1848   AT HILLSIDE, LOUISA OPENED HER SCHOOL IN THE BARN.

James K. Polk was President, 1845-1849.

Gold was discovered in California, 1848.

California became a state, 1850.

1852   LOUISA'S FIRST STORY WAS PRINTED.

Harriet Beecher Stowe's *Uncle Tom's Cabin* was published, 1852.

Stephen Foster's "Old Black Joe" was published, 1860.

The War Between the States was fought, 1861-1865.

1862   LOUISA VOLUNTEERED AS A NURSE IN THE WAR BETWEEN THE STATES.

Christopher L. Sholes built the first practical typewriter, 1867.

The first transatlantic cable was laid, 1866.

The United States purchased Alaska, 1867.

1868   LOUISA WROTE *LITTLE WOMEN*.

Alexander Graham Bell invented the telephone, 1876.

Bicycles were first made in this country, 1879.

Clara Barton founded the American Red Cross, 1881.

1888 LOUISA MAY ALCOTT DIED, MARCH 6.

There were thirty-eight states in the Union.

Grover Cleveland was President.

The population of the country was about 60,388,600.

DO YOU REMEMBER?

1. What did Louisa do and say when her Mother shut her in a dark closet?

2. How did Mr. Alcott's school differ from other schools?

3. How did Father "hold" the fire in the fireplaces overnight?

4. What food did the Alcott family *not* eat?

5. What games were played at Louisa's birthday party?

6. How did Father teach Louisa the alphabet?

7. What did Louisa do with a barrel hoop?

8. What did Louisa do at the city dump?

9. How did Father find Louisa when she was lost?

10. How did Mother punish Louisa for running away?

11. What started Louisa on her first book?

12. How did Louisa get hurt at the dock?

13. What exciting incident happened on the stage-coach on Louisa's trip to Providence?

14. Why was "Auntie" Carleton angry at Louisa?

15. What friendly deed did Mr. and Mrs. Emerson do?

16. Who was Louisa's favorite playmate?

17. What was the Alcott girls' favorite book?

18. At Fruitlands, what was used to make clothing?

19. How did Mrs. Alcott and the girls gather the barley crop?

20. How did Louisa support herself when she went to Boston to write?

IT'S FUN TO LOOK UP THESE THINGS

1. Look up the history of stagecoaches.

2. When did steel pens replace quill pens?

3. What did Ralph Waldo Emerson do?

4. What is the difference between toadstools and mushrooms?

5. What are Indian pipes?

6. For what were leather buckets used?

7. For what was Henry Thoreau noted?

196

INTERESTING THINGS YOU CAN DO

1. Tell the class the story of King Midas and the Golden Touch.

2. At the library, find a list of books written by Louisa Alcott.

3. Start a diary. Jot down interesting things you do and places you go.

4. Act out the story of Jack and the Beanstalk.

5. Make a map showing the different places where Louisa lived or to which she traveled.

6. Tell the class the story of Paul Revere.

7. Read *Little Women* and *Little Men*.

OTHER BOOKS YOU MAY ENJOY READING

Fairy Tales and Legends, Hans Christian Andersen. Macmillan.

Harriet Beecher Stowe, Connecticut Girl, Mabel Cleland Widdemer. Trade and School Editions, Bobbs-Merrill.

Katherine Lee Bates, Girl Poet, Elizabeth P. Myers. Trade and School Editions, Bobbs-Merrill.

Pinocchio, Carlo Collodi. World, Rainbow Classics.

Rebecca of Sunnybrook Farm, Kate Douglas Wiggin. Houghton Mifflin.

Secret Garden, The, Frances Hodgson Burnett. Lippincott.

INTERESTING WORDS IN THIS BOOK

admiration (ăd mĭ rā′shŭn) : awe; approval; honor

adore (à dōr′) : to worship; to admire greatly

astonishment (ăs tŏn′ĭsh mĕnt) : surprise; amazement

astounded (ăs tound′ĕd) : surprised; stunned

barley (bär′lĭ) : a kind of grain, used as cereal for humans or as food for animals

bellows (bĕl′ōz) : an instrument which draws in and expels air, for blowing a fire or filling organ pipes with wind

bewildered (bė wĭl′dērd) : confused

celebrity (sė lĕb′rĭ tĭ) : a famous person

cobblestone (kŏb′′l stōn) : a naturally rounded stone larger than a pebble

198

collide (kŏ līd') : to bump into a person or object

crane (krān) : swinging metal arm for holding an object

disgusted (dĭs gŭst'ĕd) : sickened; offended

doublet (dŭb'lĕt) : fancy, tight jacket worn by men in olden times

eerie (ē'rĭ) : ghostly; weird

ember (ĕm'bēr) : a glowing coal still burning in ashes

enthusiasm (ĕn thū'zĭ ăz'm) : zeal; interest

fable (fā'b'l) : a story not true; legend; fairy tale

fascinated (făs'ĭ nāt ĕd) : charmed

flatter (flăt'ēr) : to praise

flourish (flûr'ĭsh) : a waving or swinging motion

flurry (flûr'ĭ) : commotion

four-poster (fōr pōs'tēr) : large bedstead with four posts to support curtains

grumpy (grŭmp'ĭ) : cross; grouchy

immediately (ĭ mē'dĭ ĭt lĭ) : right away; without delay

introduce (ĭn'trŏ dūs) : to make a person known to another person

lichen (lī′kĕn) : growth on tree bark or rock

meager (mē′gẽr) : scanty; skimpy

miracle (mĭr′à k'l) : a wonderful thing which seemed impossible to happen

parasol (păr′à sŏl) : small, light, decorative umbrella

permission (pẽr mĭsh′ŭn) : consent; right

recognize (rĕk′ŏg nīz) : to know again

reflect (rė flĕkt′) : show an image or shadow

runway (rŭn′wā) : a way or track for loading

snooze (snōoz) : a short sleep; a nap

squash (skwŏsh) : a plant or vine and its fruit, of the gourd family

stooped (stōop'd) : with shoulders bent forward

sympathetic (sĭm pà thĕt′ĭk) : feeling sorry for

tanager (tăn′à jẽr) : bright-colored bird of the finch family

topple (tŏp′'l) : tumble down

undertaking (ŭn dẽr tāk′ĭng) : attempt; trial

venture (vĕn′tŭr) : project; attempt

wistfully (wĭst′fŏol lĭ) : wishfully

wriggle (rĭg′'l) : squirm